BEAVERS

BEAVERS

Andrew Kitchener

with illustrations by Ruth Pollitt

Whittet Books

FOR HAZEL AND ADAM

Cataloguing in Publication Data
A catalogue record for this title is available from the British Library

ISBN 1 873580 55 X

Printed and bound in Britain by Bookcraft

Acknowledgments

I am most grateful to the following people who have provided information and inspiration for this book:

Mairi Cole, Martin Gaywood, Derek Gow, Duncan Halley, Johan Höglund, Geoffrey Hammerson, Göran Hartman, Michelle Kay, Frank Rosell, Lars Wilsson and Derek Yalden.

I am grateful to Wildlife Biology for permission to reproduce the figure on pages 126-7 from G. Hartman 'Patterns of Spread on a reintroduced beaver population in Sweden' *Wildlife Biology* 1:97-103.

Contents

Preface	6
What is a beaver?	8
Geographical variation	10
The fossil record	15
An amphibious lifestyle	18
Dealing with vegetation	22
Castor - but not oil	25
Moving on land and in water	27
Creating a home	30
Dams	43
Changing landscapes	49
Finding food	54
Food stores	68
Choosing foods	70
Activity	71
A bad fur day	72
Scent-marking and territories	75
Making a quick escape	81
Social groups	85
Sexing beavers	87
Exploratory and threat behaviours	96
Parasites	103
Mortality	105
History in Europe	107
Fossil beavers in Britain	108
Recent history in Britain	112
Castoreum as a commodity	114
Beaver fur and hats	115
Exploitation and the New World	119
Reintroductions	123
Bringing beavers back to Britain	130
Bibliography	141
Index	142

Preface

In the summer of 1989 I was standing by a road in Virginia, when I spotted an enormous rodent swimming along minding its own business. Suddenly, my first beaver slapped its tail on the water surface and disappeared with a splash, and I saw in the same field of view a magnificent osprey lazily flapping its wings as it flew by. What I did not see was any other visible sign of beavers being present. Contrary to my preconceptions there was no clear-felled forest with numerous dead tree stumps, and there were not acres of flooded land. Had I not spotted the beaver, I would not have known it was there, but I would have unknowingly admired the magnificent wetland that its activities had created.

I had similar feelings when I visited Brittany with an enthusiastic group of beaver supporters soon after Scottish Natural Heritage had announced its decision to investigate the feasibility of reintroducing the beaver to Scotland. Although I did not see any beavers, I could at least admire their handiwork. Bushes had been skilfully coppiced many times and it took very close scrutiny to confirm that beaver incisors and not secateurs had created this abstract topiary. The dams were small and insignificant; certainly nothing to challenge any self-respecting salmon.

Little did I know that beavers would cross my professional path several times more in the next few years. As Scottish Natural Heritage (SNH) announced in 1995 that it was to investigate the feasibility of reintroducing beavers to Scotland, so I found myself in a position to contribute towards this noble aim, albeit in a small way. As Curator of Mammals and Birds of the National Museums of Scotland, I was investigating what Scottish fossil beaver specimens we have for an exhibition on the history of Scottish wildlife, which was to open in the new Museum of Scotland in 1998. One of the first requirements of the IUCN's reintroduction guidelines is to establish the former presence of a species in an area and its causes of extinction. Under contract from SNH and in collaboration with Jim Conroy of the Institute of Terrestrial Ecology (now the Centre for Ecology and Hydrology) at Banchory, we produced a comprehensive report on the history of Scotland's indigenous, but now extinct, beavers. This was followed up in 1997 by a second contract from SNH with John Lynch of Arizona State University to compare the skull morphometrics of extinct British beavers with those of extant European populations, in order to determine a suitable source population. But more of that later.

As a result of increasing numbers of headlines and other media interest, nobody can be unaware that somebody somewhere is planning a reintroduction of beavers in Scotland. This book is primarily about our former native, the Eurasian beaver, and contains only a little information about North American beavers. However, in almost all details there are very few differences between the behaviour and ecology of these two very similar species. Not only will you find out about the natural history of one of the world's most extraordinary mammals, but you will also discover how we will once again be able to welcome the beaver as a native species.

Andrew Kitchener 2001

RP 2001

What is a beaver?

With their large, robust bodies, rounded heads equipped with prominent incisor teeth and paddle-shaped scaly tails, beavers, *Castor* spp., are immediately recognisable to all. Weighing up to 38 kg and reaching almost 1.3 metres long (from nose to tail tip), beavers are the second biggest rodents in the world today, after the enormous South American capybara, *Hydrochaeris hydrochaeris*, which is not much longer than the beavers, but weighs up to almost twice as much. Only the crested porcupines, *Hystrix* spp., of Africa and southern Asia rival the beavers for size, but they are still only two thirds as long and heavy.

Although at various times in the past it has been debated as to how many beaver species there are, today it is generally accepted that there are two species, which are widely distributed throughout the northern hemisphere. Today the North American beaver, *Castor canadensis*, is found widely throughout Canada, the USA and northern Mexico, but it has also been introduced much further afield, including Europe, the Russian Far East and Patagonia. This book is primarily about the second beaver species, the Eurasian beaver, *Castor fiber*, which was once widespread throughout Europe and which still ranges as far as Mongolia and China. Although the two beaver species are known to be very distinct, it is not possible to distinguish readily between them from their external characteristics, even though it is claimed that North American beavers are smaller (see How big is a beaver?), have smaller, rounder heads, shorter, wider muzzles, thicker, longer and darker underfur, shorter, wider oval-shaped tails, and longer tibiae (shin bones) than Eurasian beavers, so that they are more able to walk on two feet. More than 27 attempts were made in captivity in Russia to hybridise these two species, and only one mating between a male North American and a female Eurasian beaver produced only a stillborn kit. These experiments reinforce the distinctiveness of the two species; also it would seem that hybridisation is very unlikely where the two species are found together. Even though I am concentrating on the Eurasian species, beaver biology is much the same for both species, but as we shall see later there are differences, which have important implications for beavers and people alike.

The two beaver species are most easily distinguished by differences between their skulls. Eurasian beavers have relatively much longer nasal bones than their North American neighbours'. The shape of the nasals is

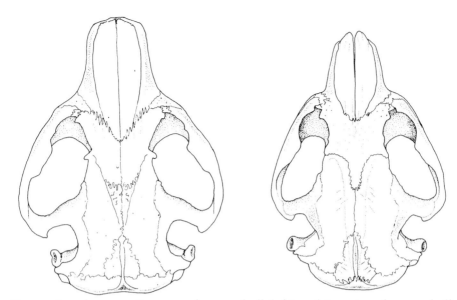

Comparison between European beaver skull (left) *and American beaver skull* (viewed from above).

also said to be different, with the widest point being at the nose end of the Eurasian's and in the middle of the North American's. The nasal aperture is said to be triangular in the Eurasian beaver and four-cornered in the North American species. Finally, the *foramen magnum* at the back of the skull, through which the spinal cord meets the brain, is supposed to be roundish in the Eurasian beaver and like an isosceles triangle that is wider than tall in the North American species. Somewhat strangely, the anal glands also differ: those of the Eurasian species are larger and thin-walled with a large internal volume, whereas the North American's are more compact with thicker walls and only a small internal volume. The significance of these differences for scent-marking is unknown. Finally the guard hairs of North American beavers have a shorter hollow medulla (central region) at their tips than those of the Eurasian beaver. The only other notable difference is the number of chromosomes, 48 in the Eurasian and only 40 in the North American. But if you happen to be in Finland or Austria, where both species occur, you may have a problem in telling them apart by counting chromosomes or measuring guard hairs.

Geographical variation

Since they have a wide distribution through Eurasia, it is not surprising that beavers show some regional variation. Up to eight different subspecies or geographical races are recognised by mammalogists today, although it should be noted that often the so-called scientific descriptions of subspecies were based on single or only a few specimens, which did not accurately reflect the variation between and within populations found throughout the beaver's geographical distribution. Also, because of severe hunting pressure and habitat loss in the past, many populations have been through bottlenecks in the past, so that today they may not reflect the original differences that were present.

The fur colour of beavers varies so that it is often said that some populations are characterised by particular colours. For example, in Belarus light chestnut-rust fur dominates, but blackish-brown beavers are most common in the Sozh River basin in Russia, while the beavers of the Voronezh Reserve also in Russia occur in about equal proportions of brown and blackish-brown. Géraldine Veron of the Museum National d'Histoire Naturelle has analysed the frequency of different colour morphs in the two beaver species and found that more than 66% of Eurasian beavers have pale brown or beige fur, about 20% have reddish brown fur, almost 8% have brown and only 4% had blackish coats. In contrast less than 50% of North American beavers have pale brown fur, more than 25% reddish brown, almost one fifth are brown and about 6% are blackish.

What is required to sort out this taxonomic uncertainty is a detailed molecular and morphological study of the different beaver populations that survive today in order to determine just how many subspecies there actually are. The most distinctive population on the basis of its large, long skull is that of the Elbe beaver, *Castor fiber albicus,* which has often been considered a separate species, although recently few mammalogists have considered this to be the case. Beavers from Asia appear to resemble North American beavers because of their shorter nasals, but despite this their skulls are still easily distinguished from those of North American beavers. However, this similarity in morphology does indicate a common Eurasian ancestor for both species (see Fossil record).

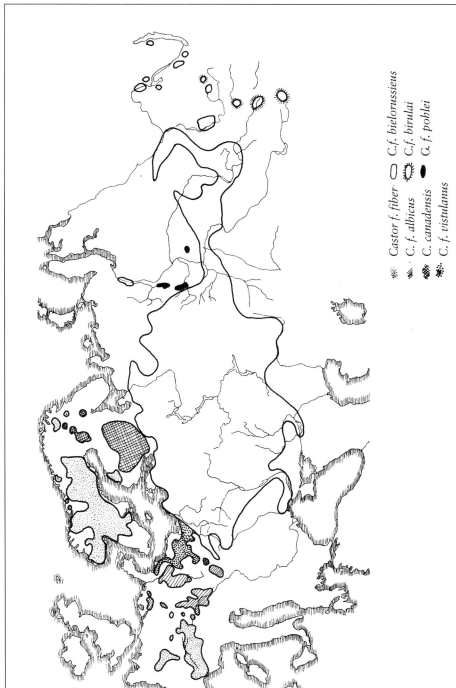

Distributions of Eurasian beaver subspecies across Europe, Russia, Mongolia and China, and the Canadian beaver in Europe.

Castor f. fiber · C.f. bielorussieus
C. f. albicus · C.f. birulai
C. canadensis · G. f. pohlei
C. f. vistulanus

The mountain beaver and the beaver-rats

Two other rodents have been given the name of beaver: the mountain beaver, Aplodontia rufa, of the moist coastal forests of north-west North America, and the beaver-rats, Hydromys *spp.* of Australia, New Guinea and surrounding islands. However, they are not closely related to beavers.

The mountain beaver's name is a particularly poor one because it not really a mountain-dwelling species and is definitely not aquatic, so its alternative name of 'sewellel' would be better used. Perhaps its rotund thickset body with its short limbs and its dense fur of sparse guard hairs with a thick underfur reminded early settlers of the real beaver? However, its apparent lack of tail has led some mammalogists to describe it as more like a giant pocket gopher or a tailless musk-rat (Ondatra zibethica). The mountain beaver weighs about one kilogramme and grows to a maximum of almost half a metre long, including its tiny 55-mm-long tail. The mountain beaver is nocturnal and spends much of its time in a burrow system complete with special chambers for holding faeces left as scent-marks. Unlike the beaver, the mountain beaver does not live in groups, although other mammals often end up sharing its burrow system including squirrels and rabbits. Mountain beavers eat a wide variety of plant material and can just about climb up to seven metres from the ground in trees in search of succulent shoots, fruits and leaves. In the autumn, mountain beavers may harvest and dry vegetation for use in their nests as well as creating a winter store of food. Like the beaver, the mountain beaver has a seasonal change in diet from deciduous leaves including fern fronds in the summer to fir needles and the bark of trees in winter.

The four species of beaver-rats are at least aquatic, but they are even more distantly related to beavers than the mountain beaver, and are often known as water-rats (not to be confused with the British water-rat which is now known as the water vole). Living in

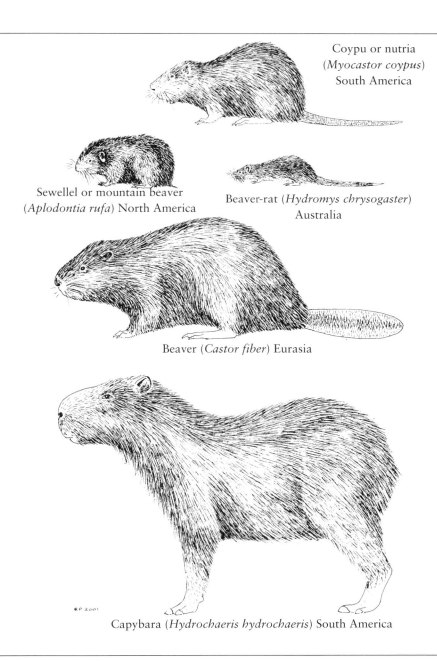

Coypu or nutria
(*Myocastor coypus*)
South America

Sewellel or mountain beaver
(*Aplodontia rufa*) North America

Beaver-rat (*Hydromys chrysogaster*)
Australia

Beaver (*Castor fiber*) Eurasia

Capybara (*Hydrochaeris hydrochaeris*) South America

water, they have aquatic adaptations including a sleek, streamlined body, partially webbed feet, nostrils set forward and eyes set high on the head, small ears and fur made up of shiny guard hairs and a dense underfur. The largest species, H. chrysogaster, is also the most widespread, being found from Tasmania to New Guinea; on average it weighs about 400 g. and grows to a total length of about just under half a metre long including a white-tipped tail of about 230 mm. Beaver-rats are found in a wide variety of habitats but are particularly common in mangrove swamps, and it is believed that their tolerance of at least partly salty water has been responsible for their wide geographical spread. Unlike the beavers and mountain beavers, beaver-rats are carnivorous, feeding on fish (up to 30 cm long!), crustaceans, aquatic insects and mussels. Beaver-rats may be active at any time of the day, but are most active at night; they rest up either in a river-bank burrow or hollow log.

One aspect unites the beavers, beaver-rats and mountain beaver: all have been exploited, often excessively at various times in the past, for their furs.

How big is a beaver?

Although beavers can reach almost 40 kg in weight, such giants are very much the exception. For example, Göran Hartman of the Swedish University of Agricultural Sciences in Uppsala has data on 148 Swedish beavers of three years or greater, showing that on average they weigh only 18 kg, ranging from 11 to 26 kg. In the Voronezh Reserve in Russia beavers range from 13 to 27 kg, which also gives a mean body weight of 18 kg. The heaviest Eurasian beaver on record weighed in at 31.7 kg.

North American beavers appear to be identical in size. Whether they are from Alabama or Maine, the average body weight of beavers two years old or more is 18 kg, with Ohio animals weighing in only slightly less with a mean of 17 kg.

The fossil record

The first beaver, *Agnotocastor galushai*, appeared in the fossil record of the late Eocene and early Oligocene (about 35 million years ago) in what we call today Natrona County, Wyoming, USA. The beaver family went through a major radiation during the Oligocene and spread to Europe by the late Oligocene and to Asia by the early Miocene. Twenty-four genera of beavers are known including *Castor*, which first appeared in western Europe (Germany) in the upper Miocene (more than 10 million years ago), and then later in the early Pliocene in what is known today as Shansi in China, and Mongolia. The small marmot-sized *Steneofiber* of the Oligocene and Miocene, followed by *Palaeomys*, are thought to be the direct ancestors of *Castor*, which is known from North America from the mid to late Pliocene (3-5 million years ago). Today's Eurasian species dates from the late Pliocene/early Pleistocene less than two million years ago, whereas the North American beaver has been around for only half that time. Most of the beaver genera disappeared from the fossil record by the end of the Pliocene. Clearly, today's two species are all we have to show for a once diverse family of rodents.

Beavers have a good fossil record, because they are big (as far as rodents go) and because lake and river deposits in which they are usually found are good for preservation. Dams also tend to collect bodies such as probably occurred in the deposits of the Forest Bed of Norfolk. Through its long evolutionary history the beaver family has shown increasing hypsodonty (high cheek teeth), presumably as the beavers have become adapted to tougher diets, which produced more wear on the teeth.

Although we are very familiar with the wood-working and dam-building skills of today's beavers, ancient beavers often had completely different lifestyles. For example, curious helical structures called devil's corkscrews or *daimonelix* have been found as fossils dating from the Oligocene and Miocene (17-28 million years ago) of Nebraska, USA. These curious structures are the in-filled remains of tight vertical corkscrew tunnels, leading to a chamber 2.5 metres below the surface. These tunnels were originally gnawed into semi-arid sandy upland deposits by a now extinct beaver, *Palaeocastor*, which was about the size of today's muskrat.

Perhaps the most extraordinary beaver was another North American species, but which dated from the Pleistocene (less than 1.6 million years ago), *Castoroides ohioensis*, and whose fossil ancestry can be traced back

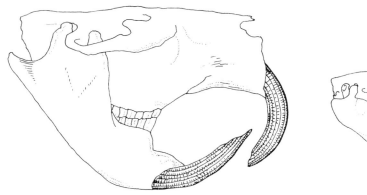

Comparison between Castoroides ohioensis (left) *and* Castor fiber *(Eurasian beaver).*

to *Dipoides* and *Eucastor*. It grew almost as large as the American black bear, *Ursus americanus*, measuring 2.5 metres long and probably weighing up to 200 kilogrammes. However, despite being the largest beaver ever known, its brain was only as big as those of the beavers of today. To some extent *Castoroides* was similar to today's beavers with its small front feet and large (probably) webbed hind feet, but its legs were relatively shorter and its tail was relatively longer and narrower. Its incisor teeth extended only 100 mm from the gum line and had rounded blunt tips, like the capybara's, for cutting and grinding coarse swamp vegetation. It did not build dams and its teeth could not have felled trees, so it is believed to have led a rather coypu-like lifestyle, lazily floating in the water and chomping its way through less demanding greenery than the beavers of today. Fossil *Castoroides* have been found from Alaska to Florida, but are particularly common in the Great Lakes region. The Athabascan-speaking people of north-west North America have a legend concerning the presence of giant beavers in their lands. Whether this is really a story passed down the generations from the earliest times based on actual experience of *Castoroides*, which became extinct only 12,000 years ago, or whether it has been inspired by the discovery of fossil bones is not known. However, it is very intriguing!

From the beginning until the early middle of the Pleistocene, some 1.6

million to about 300,000 years ago, Europe was also home to the Eurasian giant beaver (*Trogontherium cuvieri*), which was a bit bigger than the Eurasian beaver, but which did not have a broad flattened tail. From the structure of the premaxillae of the skull, it has been suggested that *Trogontherium* had a muscular, prehensile split lip, which it used to grab succulent aquatic vegetation (e.g. pond weed *Potamogeton*, arrowhead *Sagittaria*, water crowfoot *Ranunculus* and water mint *Mentha aquatica*). However, a reanalysis of the skull anatomy by Robert Mayhew of Cambridge University came to a different conclusion: *Trogontherium* had very similar jaw musculature and teeth to *Castoroides* and almost certainly led a similar coypu-like lifestyle on the lower reaches of rivers and in lowland lakes on flood plains. Its teeth had only a thin layer of enamel and were round in cross-section, indicating that they would not have been used to gnaw through wood, but they may have been used to prise bark off trees.

The earliest beavers of the genus *Castor* are known from the end of the Pliocene and beginning of the Pleistocene of Europe. These early beavers are often considered to be a distinct species, *Castor plicidens*, but studies of tooth wear in modern beavers suggest that these fossils probably just belong to very old individuals of *Castor fiber*. Beavers first appeared in the fossil record of North America in the upper Pliocene, having crossed the Bering land bridge from eastern Asia. Both of today's beavers still share a nematode parasite of the gut, *Travossius rufus*, (in Scandinavian and eastern European populations only for *C. fiber*) and the ectoparasitic beaver beetle, *Platypsyllus castoris* (see p.103). Therefore, both beaver species have a common ancestor that dates back to the end of the Pliocene, or the North American species may be a direct descendent of the Eurasian species as suggested by the intermediate skull morphology of Asian forms.

An amphibious lifestyle

Beavers are renowned not only for their work ethic and family values, but also for their ability to construct dams across rivers and lodges as homes. In order to pursue this amphibious lifestyle, beavers show adaptations for life on land and in the water. As with many aquatic mammals, beavers' eyes, ears and nostrils are set high on their heads so that they can sense their environment even while swimming on the surface of the water. To prevent the entry of water, the nostrils have special round sphincters (circular muscles) that close up tightly when beavers dive underwater. Their ear flaps have special muscles that allow them to fold along their lengths to prevent water entering the ears. There is also dense fluffy hair inside the ears, which traps air, thereby preventing water seeping in to them. Both the nose and ears automatically close up as the beaver's nose touches the water. In order to provide protection and avoid discomfort underwater, the eyes have a third, clear eyelid, the nictitating membrane, which also allows them to see unhindered underwater.

In common with marine mammals, but also horses, beavers have an epiglottis (a flap that closes over the wind-pipe) inside the nasal cavity rather than at the back of the throat as in people. In humans the epiglottis prevents food and drink from entering the wind-pipe accidentally while eating, drinking and swallowing. In beavers it also prevents water entering

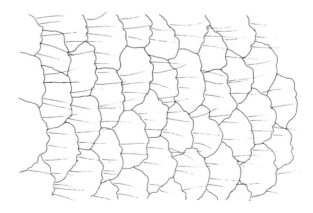

Detail of tail scales with hairs in between (three times larger than life).

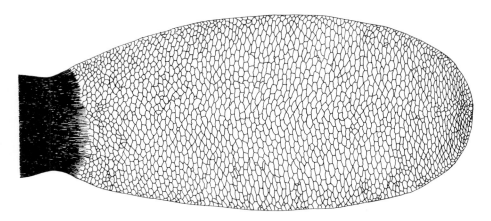

The scaly tail of a Eurasian beaver.

the wind-pipe when swimming and diving. As a consequence of this anatomical specialisation, beavers cannot breathe or pant through their mouths. They can drink or eat semi-liquid food without displacing the epiglottis, but it must be retracted if they swallow solid foods. Just to make absolutely sure no water gets into the wind-pipe accidentally, the middle of the upper surface of the back of the tongue is raised up so that at rest it fits snugly into the back of the oral cavity. Therefore, beavers can safely gnaw off stems and roots of aquatic plants and branches of partly submerged trees underwater without the risk of breathing in water accidentally.

Beavers have sleek, torpedo-shaped bodies when swimming underwater, thereby minimising drag and wastage of energy. The hind feet are generously webbed to provide the essential thrust when swimming and the flattened scaly tail (with its parallel sides in the Eurasian species) can be used as an oar to scull through the water or as a flipper to propel a beaver when it is in a hurry. The tail consists of thick fatty tissue, through which thick tendons

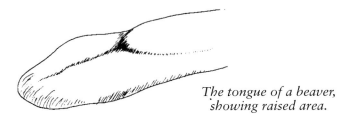

The tongue of a beaver,
showing raised area.

Section through the fur of a beaver showing short dense underfur and longer guard hairs.

run from short powerful muscles at the base of the tail. Beaver tails are not only used for locomotion, but store fat and are used in thermoregulation. For example, beavers have been seen sitting with their tails tucked underneath them, warming their hind feet. The fur consists of pale dense underfur, which is almost like grey cotton wool in appearance and to the touch, and longer, stiffer dark guard hairs (about 60 mm long in the summer pelage and 65 mm long in winter), which help repel the water. As a result a layer of air is trapped by the fur, which can give a silvery appearance to the diving beaver. Like otters, beavers rely mainly on their fur to insulate them against the cold when in the water as well as on land, but unlike otters they have not successfully colonised coasts. Some beavers have been recorded

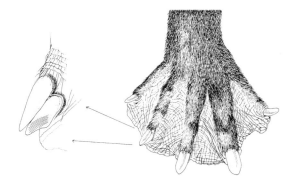

Hind foot and grooming claw.

swimming in the sea off the west coast of Sweden, so at least occasionally beavers may presumably disperse between rivers via the coast. It is likely that sea water would damage the insulating properties of beaver fur, as it does with otter fur, which may explain why beavers have not colonised coasts permanently. Beavers have two moults of their fur each year: the spring moult is from April to the beginning of May and the more intense autumn moult is from the end of August to the end of September. Most individuals moult over a period of six days, but males tend to moult earlier than females.

Beavers need to maintain their fur in excellent condition, so that it keeps them dry and warm, especially when swimming. It is no surprise that they spend much time grooming, using both their fore and hind feet. The hind feet have a special adaptation for this purpose: the second toe has a double claw, which can be opened up, when the toe is bent, to create a simple comb. This comb is especially efficient at removing ticks, *Schizocarpus minguandi*, which are very small and often occur in very large numbers. It has been suggested that the combing claws are used to smear anal gland secretion over the fur, thereby waterproofing it, but recent research by Frank Rosell suggests that this use of anal gland secretion is unlikely.

Beavers have physiological adaptations to diving. We are only able to exchange about 15% of the air in our lungs as we breathe, but beavers can achieve a remarkable 75% so that they can stay longer underwater than we can. Beavers also maintain an oxygen-rich blood supply to the brain while underwater and can tolerate high levels of carbon dioxide like many other aquatic mammals, but unlike us. Beavers can also reduce their heart beat rate (bradycardia) to about half of normal levels while diving (a mean of 67 beats/minute versus a mean of 125), thus reducing their rate of use of oxygen.

R P 2001

Dealing with vegetation

The most prominent adaptation for dealing with a woody diet is the beavers' very large, curved, orange incisors. As with all rodent incisors, they have open roots (if a tooth has an open root, it will continue to grow; if the root closes up, it will stop growing and eventually wear down) so that they grow throughout life, and have a very hard enamel outer surface backed by softer dentine. Differential wear of these two materials leads to a sharp cutting edge. Intermittently while chewing, beavers stop about every ten minutes or so to re-sharpen their teeth(see p. 66). When biting, beavers mainly use their upper incisors to hold the woody vegetation and bite against them using the lower incisors.

Again, like other rodents, beavers do not have canine teeth, but instead there is a gap in the toothrow called a diastema, which allows beavers to pull in their lips to close up their mouths, in order to stop unwanted sawdust and other waste vegetation getting into their mouths while gnawing, and to prevent water entering the mouth when swimming along with vegetation held in the incisors or when gnawing aquatic plants underwater. The chewing teeth consist of one pair of premolars and three pairs of molars in the upper and lower jaws, giving a total of 20 in all

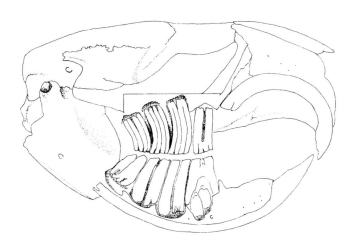

Lateral view of a beaver skull with bone removed to show the roots of the teeth.

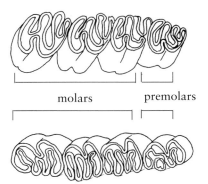

*A beaver's chewing teeth: upper jaw (*top*) and lower jaw (*bottom*). The nose is towards the right.*

compared with our more numerous 32. The chewing teeth are made up of folds of hard enamel in-filled with softer dentine and cementum. As with the incisors, the chewing teeth rely on differential wear between the tooth materials to maintain sharp chewing blades as the flat surfaces grind against each other. Unlike the incisors the high cheek teeth have roots that close eventually, so that they wear down gradually throughout the beaver's life. If they live to old age, the teeth may eventually wear out. The number of enamel folds decreases with age as the teeth wear down, leaving eventually only cementum and dentine, which are useless for grinding up vegetation. Unlike people, beavers do not chew by moving their lower jaws from side to side, but instead the lower jaw slides back and forth to grind up the food. The incisors and chewing teeth are offset from each other so that they cannot be used at the same time. In order to gnaw, the lower jaw must slide forward so that the incisors engage with each other leaving the chewing teeth unaffected. The opposite is the case for the chewing teeth. In this way unnecessary wear and damage to the sets of teeth can be avoided when they are not needed for their respective functions.

Beavers are mainly nocturnal so their tactile sense is very important to them. They have well-developed whiskers on their heads, mostly four or five long, stiff whiskers (up to 90 mm long) between the eyes and nose on each side of the head. There are also small tufts above the eyes and large groups of whiskers of varying lengths on the muzzle above the lips.

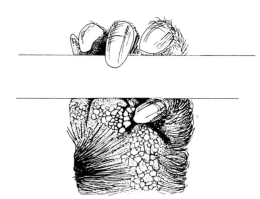

A beaver's left hand holding a branch using its 'little finger' like a thumb.

All herbivorous mammals face the problem of how to digest cellulose. Unfortunately for beavers they do not have a rumen like bovids (cattle, sheep, goats and antelopes), but have to rely on their caecum (hind gut), where microorganisms produce enzymes that digest the cellulose. Digestion occurs only at a very low efficiency of about 30% (compared with 44% of protein), and it takes about 60 hours for food to pass through a beaver. The problem is that the hind gut cannot absorb much of the cellulose break-down products and so beavers have to overcome this in two ways. Firstly, they must eat an enormous amount of food each day; up to about 2 kg of bark per day or about 10% of average body weight. Secondly, they produce special green faeces, while sitting upright on the ground with their tails running forward, which they ingest so that it can be further digested and the nutrients absorbed in the stomach and upper intestines. This process occurs in other rodents and lagomorphs and is known as coecotrophy or coprophagy.

Beavers are renowned for their construction skills and are very adept while feeding. For this they rely on their dextrous hands, which, unlike the hind feet, are not webbed. They even have an opposable digit so that they can easily grasp food or materials, but unlike our thumb (the first digit), the beavers use their fifth digit (our 'little finger') for this purpose.

Although we think of beavers as being terrestrial and aquatic rodents, some individuals are quite good at climbing. In Belarus an aspen tree had fallen across a ditch and was at least 1.5 metres above the water. A beaver managed to climb across the tree to gnaw away the bark in the middle!

Castor – but not oil

The beaver's scientific name *Castor* is commonly believed to have originated from an unconfirmed observation dating from Ancient Greek times (Aesop's Fables no less!) of its predator escape behaviour and a confusion about its anatomy. On being chased by dogs, male beavers were said to castrate themselves, thereby leaving the object of the hunt, their testes, for the pursuing hunter. If the castrated beaver were hunted again, it would run up to an elevated spot and lift its leg to show that it had already sacrificed its testes and was, therefore, not worth hunting. Some enterprising beavers were apparently able to hide their testes internally and so avoid castration in the first place; this was presumably based on genuine observations that the beaver's testes are held within the body cavity. I am sure that you can see a number of problems with this story; for example, castoreum (see p.76) is produced by the castor sacs and not by the testes, which would not have been visible anyway. Frequent

A medieval beaver avoids predation by castrating itself.

I said, 'Can I have my ball back?'

self-castration would have presumably ultimately led to the beaver's extinction. Surprisingly, no modern observers of beavers have recorded this behaviour!

The Greek word for the beaver, *καστωρ*, was Latinised to *Castor*, and is thought to be derived from Indo-European words for musk gland and musk of the musk deer, *Moschus* spp., such as the Sanskrit *kasturi* and *kastora*, presumably referring to castoreum. I am sure you will agree that this is a much more convincing explanation for the origin of the beaver's generic name.

As for *fiber*, this was the Roman name for the beaver and it is believed to have its roots also in Indo-European languages such as the Sanskrit *babhru* or the Old Aryan word *bebhrus*, which roughly translates as the colour brown often relating to the brown bear, *Ursus arctos*. Variations of these words became the vernacular name for the beaver throughout Europe (involving the substitution of 'b' for 'f' or 'v'), including *beber* (Gallic), *befer* (Old Cornish), *beofer* (Old English), *bibaro* (Spanish), *bevero* (Italian), *bièvre* (French), etc.

Moving on land and in water

On land beavers are rather ungainly. When foraging or working on their construction sites, they use a slow diagonal limb coordination if walking on all-fours. They also amble along on two hind feet when carrying materials and food, but they can move faster by galloping. As with any behaviours, beaver kits walk in a fully coordinated manner just a few hours after they are born, but galloping is not fully developed until about one month old, when their escape response is also fully developed. Young beavers do not need to show any bipedal walking until their first autumn when they help with lodge and dam construction or maintenance, but they are able to walk upright much earlier than this.

In the water it is a different story. Beavers are probably the most aquatic of all rodents and they can move fast underwater for long distances. They prefer to use the water for transporting material and food because it is much easier and exposes the beavers to less risk of predation than when on land. Because their forepaws are often tied up with grasping or holding items when swimming, beavers use only their hind limbs for propulsion, pushing backwards alternately with each webbed hind foot. Even when carrying nothing, beavers still hold their forepaws under their necks. At

Diving from surface.

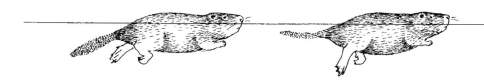

first young beavers may use all four limbs when swimming, but they soon learn to swim like their parents and older siblings. Beaver kits are able to swim at only four days old and can dive by twelve days.

The tail may also contribute to the swimming action by moving from side to side and thereby acting as a sculling oar, especially when swimming fast. The tail may also assist in dives, but not when tail-slapping (see below). Beavers change their direction when swimming by making powerful strokes with one leg and twisting their tails and lower backs.

Usually beavers dive almost silently, barely making a ripple at the water's surface, but if they are alarmed, they arch their tails over their backs and slap them down violently on the water surface. This tail slapping probably has two main functions, but does not enhance the speed of the dive. Firstly, it alerts predators to the fact that they have been seen, and the beavers are not worth pursuing. Secondly, tail slapping alerts other group members to the presence of possible danger. Young beavers learn

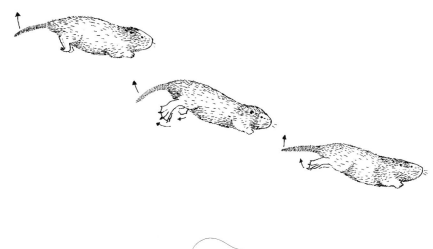

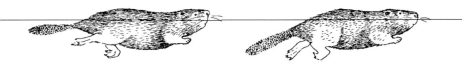

how to avoid danger very early; from one month old they slap their tails before diving and by two months their ability to remain under water when frightened is as good as that of the adults.

When diving beavers make powerful synchronous strokes of the hind legs if completely underwater and also their bodies and tails make undulating movements. If they are trying to pass through a narrow gap or are near the bottom, they are well able to swim along using only these undulations. The tail is used like a hydrofoil under water to elevate the diving beaver when it wants to return to the surface.

The beaver's diving statistics are impressive. It can reach a maximum swimming speed of 2.1 metres per second and can remain underwater for up to 15 minutes. However, if it is moving or working underwater, maximum dive times are in the region of 4-5 minutes. Beavers have been recorded swimming up to 800 metres underwater, which equates to some 6.4 minutes underwater assuming the maximum swimming speed.

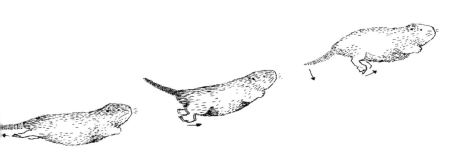

Creating a home

When beavers colonise a new area, it is important that they find some kind of shelter to avoid predators and the winter weather. Often they will take advantage of existing holes in the riverbank or even caves, but more often they will develop a tunnel and lodge system to allow for better protection and for a larger colony to develop, particularly where natural openings are few and far between, and where the water may be too shallow for safe diving to escape predators. During the summer, when the male and young beavers from previous years may leave the lodge to the breeding female, beavers create temporary dens in steep river banks, where they are hidden by dense vegetation. Dispersing young beavers may make similar temporary homes. Dams may be needed to create a large area of deep water into which they can escape easily while foraging, and to allow for a water-filled moat to the lodge, thereby providing even greater protection for its inhabitants. It is not surprising, therefore, to find that beavers are expert tunnellers, wood workers, stone masons, hydrologists, plasterers and architects. However, let us begin with digging, which is usually where beavers begin when building a new home.

Digging

When they find a natural depression or existing hole in the riverbank, beavers may dig into it by using alternating arm movements to scratch away the soil with the paws. They may dig for five to ten minutes at a time before taking a breather. They then may move the waste material in one of five ways: shovelling, pushing, backing, sweeping and shoving. Although most of these behaviours are shown by many other rodents, shoving seems to be unique to beavers and is mainly associated with building. Shovelling involves using the hind paws to shovel back the waste material generated by the forepaws and is alternated with the scratching digging actions. Where the earth has not been shovelled away, it may be swept to the side using the forelegs. When a pile of earth builds up to the side or behind the digging beaver, it stops, turns round and stretches its arms forwards to push the pile along. It uses similar behaviour to push building materials to the lodge or dam construction site. A beaver may also move backwards (backing), pushing the pile with alternate movements of its forepaws. In contrast, when digging below water level, the beaver

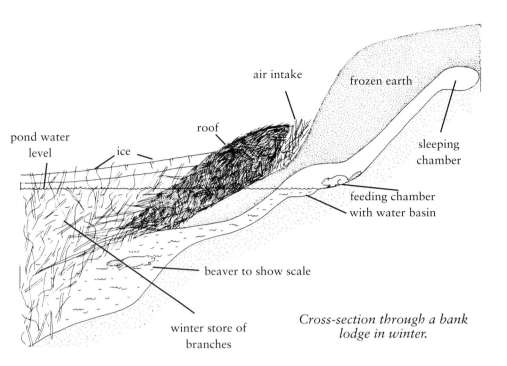

air intake

frozen earth

roof

pond water
level

ice

sleeping
chamber

feeding chamber
with water basin

beaver to show scale

*Cross-section through a bank
lodge in winter.*

winter store of
branches

emerges periodically with a pile of earth, which it pushes out with its paws. The beaver may pack soil and other materials against the walls of tunnels, dams and lodges with its nose, exposed incisors or forepaws, while digging and building.

Beavers may sleep together, but they certainly do not like digging together, which is why tunnel systems may become quite extensive and separated from each other. If a beaver tries to muscle in on another's digging site, the digger whines until the trespasser goes away.

As usual, young beavers are incredibly precocious when it comes to digging. Kits begin scratching, shovelling and pushing earth at only 14 days old and by two months of age they can build their own temporary burrows to rest in. Also at this age beaver kits are able to dig holes located at natural depressions in the bank of the river. By their first autumn, young beavers have developed the full set of digging actions, including sweeping, pushing, shoving and backing. By their second summer, young beavers are able to dig underwater, resulting in a typical tunnel and chamber system.

Tunnels and chambers

Beavers do not necessarily live in lodges all year round. Simple burrows are often created as temporary hiding places in summer or by dispersing young beavers. These are not normally more than five metres long and most have two entrances, usually above water level. These temporary dens have soft bedding of dried leaves, debarked wood and twigs.

Permanent burrows always have tunnels with their entrances below the water surface. The beavers begin by digging out the floor of the tunnel where it passes the water surface to create a water-filled channel or basin. Then shelves are excavated in the walls of the tunnel surrounding the water to create the feeding chamber. Here the beavers can sit, groom and feed while in or beside the water, and feel totally secure. If the riverbanks are high enough, sleeping chambers are then dug out safely above the water level at the ends of the tunnels to avoid flooding when water levels rise. The pattern of digging a tunnel system is usually inwards and horizontal, in order to form the feeding chamber, and then further inland and upwards to create the sleeping chambers. Permanent burrows may become lodges depending on how the group develops and the structure of the bank.

Burrows rarely have a single entrance, but normally have at least two or three, even as many as seven. The entrance to the burrow has to be big (30-56 cm in diameter) to allow a large beaver to enter, and the burrows are usually found 0.75 to 1.5 metres below the ground surface and may extend some 4 to 10 metres inland. A chamber is constructed either at the end of the burrow or often halfway along, which in Russia has been recorded as being about one metre in diameter and 25-40 cm high. The floor of this chamber is lined with small twigs, bits of wood and chips of wood gnawed from trees. These kinds of chamber often fill up with feeding remains, which must either be removed or the earth ceiling of the chamber may be excavated to create the necessary head room. These complex burrows may eventually develop into bank lodges (see p.34).

On the Rhone in France beavers rarely build lodges; 95% of beaver nests are either in natural or excavated burrows or in bank lodges. The tunnels are 0.8-11 metres long and 30-50 cm high with a nest chamber of 50-80 cm in diameter.

A beaver drags a branch along a canal.

Canals

Beavers may also create canals from the main water body, partly by habitual use of a pathway resulting in erosion, but also by digging and throwing the waste to the sides. These canals are vital for a quick get-away from foraging areas, in case beavers are surprised by predators or other disturbances. They also make it much easier for transporting materials and food back to the water. Where canals run close to lodges, the beavers may construct a roof over them, rather like the roofs over bank lodges (see p.34). Canals are generally 0.2 to one metre in depth, averaging half a metre deep, and 0.3-0.6 metres wide. If water levels are likely to vary within the canals, small earthen dams may be built or logs may be used to block the canal to maintain water levels. Canals may be several hundred metres long; among the longest recorded in the Voronezh Reserve in Russia was one about 200 metres long, which branched several times as it led into foraging areas. The longest canal on record was constructed by North American beavers in Montana and ran for an astonishing 420 metres.

Temporary nests

In areas where severe floods may occur so that lodges and burrows become temporarily uninhabitable, beavers have been known to build temporary nests or couches. In the Voronezh Reserve these have been recorded as a large mass of twigs that have been placed in bushes above the flood water. One such structure of one metre square was found in Lipetsk County on the Voronezh River and was about 2.5 metres above the ground and more than 3 metres above the water. However, in other areas beavers apparently need fewer creature comforts and just make do with taking refuge on fallen trees, tree stumps or mounds sticking out of the water.

Lodges

In colder climates beavers spend their winters in lodges to escape from the severe winter weather and predators. Lodges are also where females give birth to young in early summer. Lodges require a great deal of time, materials and effort to construct, so that it is not surprising that the same lodge may be used continuously for many years. For example, in the Osinka Forest Lake in Russia one lodge was recorded as being occupied for 40 years. It has been calculated that it takes about 20 days for a beaver group to construct a lodge from scratch.

On the River Faxälv in Sweden beavers retire to their lodges when ice begins to form on the water in October. Just to show how cosy and warm lodges are, temperatures inside a lodge in Ontario, Canada, were recorded as being between 0.8°C to 1.6°C when the external air temperatures were between –6.8°C and –21°C, and there was no snow cover to offer an extra layer of insulation. Temperatures in the lodge were higher when the beavers were at home, generally at night, and fell in the early morning and afternoon when the beavers were active outside. Temperatures were also recorded during the summer in an empty lodge

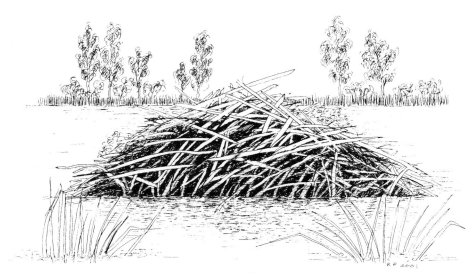

Brook lodge.

on the Voronezh River in Russia and were found to be similar to those in the soil at a depth of 25 cm and never varied by more than 3.2°C. The capillary action of the wood and mud of the lodge makes its internal atmosphere very humid and mould often grows on the well-clipped, smooth walls even though they may be more than 2 metres above the water surface.

Beavers build two main kinds of lodge: bank lodges and brook lodges. Bank lodges are the only kind of lodge that is built along main rivers, but they are usually found only on tributaries, where the banks are high enough to allow the beavers to dig tunnels. Where the banks are too low for this, beavers tend to build conical brook lodges.

Bank lodges often start out as bank dens, which are later extended to house a growing group of beavers, or they are newly built following the normal bank den plan with its hidden entrances below water, feeding chamber at water level and sleeping dens further inland and at a higher level to avoid flooding. The beavers then build a roof of sticks over the tunnel and generally also the feeding chamber. The roof is covered in loose bark and twigs, and is plastered with mud from the riverbed, thereby consolidating the structure and preventing it from eroding, as well as sealing it from the elements to provide frost-free and ice-free conditions in the water-filled tunnels and feeding chambers.

The part of the roof furthest inland (and hence the most dangerous part to work on as far as potential predation goes) is left unsealed and it has been suggested that this allows for the lodge to be ventilated, especially when the ground is frozen. Since beavers may not emerge for many days at a time from their lodges in winter, a good air-handling system is an absolute must. However, some lodges are completely plastered over with mud and burrows have no 'ventilation system'; because they are diving mammals, beavers are able to tolerate high levels of carbon dioxide and low levels of oxygen. So perhaps the lack of plastering reflects the difficulty of getting the mud there in the first place. If the earth roof of the feeding chamber collapses later, there is, therefore, already a protective roof in place. The structure of the bank may not allow the beavers to build a concealed entrance into the water, and in these cases the roof is extended into the water to create a new underwater entrance. There may be more than one tunnel system under one roof, with no interconnections between them. Old lodges are renovated every autumn using alternate layers of branches and finer material such as bark or twigs with mud.

As mentioned earlier, beavers may be forced to build conical brook lodges where the banks of the river or lake are too low for tunnelling or where the substrate is rocky or stony thereby being impossible to excavate. These may also start out as simple bank burrows or bank lodges excavated

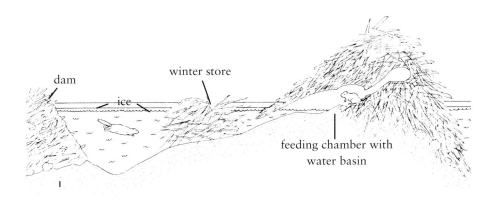

Cross-section through a brook lodge in winter. Note the dam is usually much further from the lodge than shown in this diagram.

A beaver swims into the underwater entrance of a lodge.

into the river bank, but as the wooden construction grows and water levels rise from dam building, so the lodge becomes conical in shape and is generally surrounded by water. To create a new brook lodge, the beavers build a compact pile of wood and other building materials and then gnaw away inside until they have created a feeding chamber with its own water basin, and also a sleeping chamber sufficiently large for the beaver colony.

It is important to note that the feeding chamber is always at the water level so that food and waste can be brought into and removed from the lodge with minimum effort. A great advantage of a brook lodge is that it can be built on stony or rocky ground, because tunnels are not necessary in its construction and the dams raise water levels to conceal the entrances into the lodge. Like bank lodges, the part of lodge closest to the land is not sealed with mud. When the lodge is completely surrounded by water, the apex of the conical lodge remains unplastered. There may be a tunnel system leading from the brook lodge, which can be very extensive. On the River Faxälv in Sweden a complex tunnel system measuring more than 100 metres was dug into banks surrounding a lodge and dam system. Lodges are enlarged for the growing colony by increasing the chamber size from within and only adding material to the outside if the external walls become too thin. The feeding chamber of a lodge on Lake Chernoe in Belarus was 53 cm high and 178 cm in diameter, below a roof 35 cm thick. However, the internal chambers may be very large, measuring up to 4 metres long by 2.5 metres wide with a ceiling height of 0.6 metres.

Lodges may also be constructed on floating mats of vegetation so that they rise and fall with varying water levels, or they may be based around the roots of alder or willow trees or bushes. In areas where spring flooding is frequent after the snow melts, lodges may have a variety of levels, so that the beaver colony can escape the rising water levels. For example, a giant lodge on the Ivnitsa River, in the Voronezh Reserve, had five stories, of which two were underwater to allow for access to the lodge at different depths of water. Often one of the underwater levels may be expanded into a storeroom where food can be kept over the winter.

Lodges may grow to enormous sizes, especially if colonies are resident for many years. For example, among the largest lodges recorded in Norway was one that reached a height of 2 metres and a diameter of 14 metres, while another monster lodge on the Ivnitsa River in the Voronezh Reserve in Russia reached 2.5 metres tall and 12 metres in diameter. These were equivalent in size to the largest North American lodges; for example one in California was 2.1 metres tall with a diameter of 8 metres. Voronezh lodges are more usually only 0.7 to 2 metres high and 1.5-3.5 metres in diameter.

Building lodges

Beavers mostly begin building or renovating their lodges in the autumn as temperatures begin to fall, although pregnant females may also be stimulated to start building when their young are born in early summer. For new lodges the beavers may respond to openings, cracks or depressions in the ground at the chosen site, as well as being influenced by external factors, including the scent-marks of other beavers. Much of the construction behaviour and its timing appears to be instinctive, as single beavers and those isolated artificially from their parents at a very early age will build just as intensively as an existing colony. However, if the established pair in a group is removed, the building work stops immediately for that year. Lodge building also occurs only where a pair of beavers is totally familiar with their home range, so that late arrivals to a new area will postpone their lodge building until the following autumn. In their nightly routine, beavers concentrate first on getting themselves fed and then spend the later part of the night building, but if time is short before winter begins, they may spend the whole night in construction.

Another important stimulus for lodge building is rising water levels. Where bank tunnels become flooded with water, the beavers begin immediately to build a lodge above them. However, not all beavers are stimulated to build lodges. If the sleeping chamber is dug out in the bank far from the water, the beavers do not generally build a lodge above it, even if the earth roof of the chamber collapses, exposing it to the surface. In this case the beavers construct a roof just sufficient to enclose the chamber again.

Lodges are mainly constructed from branches and other coarser materials, which are heaped in a disorderly manner at the construction site. Beavers are stimulated to put more material on to the heap unless they become distracted by something else such as a depression in the ground nearby; they usually carry or drag building materials up a slope, rather than down one. Longer branches are dragged to the top of the heap and then pinned against the backside of the lodge in order to support the structure. If any holes or gaps develop as the heap increases in size, the beavers fill these by pinning smaller branches in the spaces or filling them with finer material such as mud. Eventually the beavers create a smooth face to the lodge, which also acts as an insulating layer.

With all this coming and going between the water and the lodge during construction, the beavers create a well-trampled road all the way to the top of the heap, which, once it is smooth, often results in more major construction material being heaped on top of the pile. Any gaps are filled in as the beavers notice them. Mud and other finer materials are plastered on the gently-sloping side of the lodge facing the water from water level upwards, while the opposite steep, land-facing side is left unplastered (see above). If the lodge becomes surrounded by water as a result of dam building, this plastering process continues around the whole perimeter of the lodge, leaving a conical shape with an unplastered apex. Beavers begin to use a new lodge when it is about one metre high and two metres in diameter.

There is an interesting feedback mechanism between lodge and dam building. After dams have been built and the water level rises, this stimulates the building of lodges. As the building activity is switched from dams to the lodge, so it automatically checks the continued building of dams. In this way, an equilibrium is eventually established with an appropriate water level for the main lodge.

Building materials and construction skills

Beavers use a variety of materials for dam and lodge construction, ranging from stones and rocks, which are often used at the bases of their constructions, to pieces of wood of a wide variety of lengths and diameters, and twigs, leaves, mud and gravel, which are used to seal dams off so that they are water tight, or to insulate lodges from the cold.

Beavers are renowned for their building skills, but they have to be able to transport materials to the appropriate place in order to construct dams, lodges and other structures. When trying to move a long piece of wood, a beaver grabs it at one end and drags the wood along while swimming or walking. They often use the leftover pieces of wood and twigs from feeding for dam or lodge construction. When they emerge from the lodge

A beaver dragging a branch while swimming.

each morning this waste is carried out and is either used immediately for construction or it is dumped in the water where it accumulates throughout the year for later use. All the beavers have to do is collect these materials from the river or pond bed, without any risk of going on to land. Also the water may help support the load. Shorter pieces of wood and finer material such as mud, gravel, twigs and leaves are carried in the beaver's mouth, having been lifted up by one or both paws, and often involving rapid alternation of its grip with both paws until it has a firm hold. However, most finer material is carried under the chin, being held in place by the forelegs; the beaver first pushes the material into its mouth and then pushes the palms of its hands on the ground under even more material, which creates a bundle which is pushed under the chin. The hands are then pushed along the ground, shoving the burden along. A beaver may also just push materials along in front of it.

When carrying a bundle of material along uneven ground, a beaver may be forced to get up on its hind legs and walk along bipedally, holding the material in its outstretched arms and using its tail as a counterbalance. Beavers can carry or shove material over great distances, usually on more or less level ground or up a slope. When the beaver reaches the construction site, the materials are lifted on top of any that may have already been collected.

Beavers pin branches and sticks into position by grabbing them near one end with their incisors and near the other end with a forepaw, and using one of their paws to guide the stick towards a hole or gap, while using jerky head movements to drive the stick firmly home. Earth and other fine materials are generally packed against the sides of dams or lodges using the palms of the forepaws; chins, noses or the flat face of the incisors are also used to tightly push this finer material into place. Beavers are very adept at creating finer material for lining the walls of the lodge or to provide soft bedding, by peeling wood into fine strips from sticks to create a kind of wood wool.

As with much beaver behaviour, lodge building appears to be innate. Young beavers of only 14 days old may start carrying sticks or pushing other building materials. They can drag branches from the water only a few days later and by 23 days old they can pin sticks into the lodge. By 45 days old beaver kits are showing all the building movements displayed by adults, including the piling of wet leaves and twigs on to the lodge, and shoving, lifting and packing with the nose and forepaws. At first young

In medieval times beavers were thought to transport logs like this!

beavers' building attempts are scattered and random, but by the autumn they localise their activities at one site just like the adults. Even without parental influence, all young beavers are capable of building their own lodges in their first autumn when only about six months old.

Dams

The most primitive dams are made only of earth and are most often built on beaver canals or across narrow streams. More major constructions involving a variety of materials are built on larger water courses with faster flows of water. However, beavers do not usually build dams on the largest rivers and tributaries, because the water flows may be too great to resist. Several separate dams may be built on smaller estuaries or on floodplains, mostly downstream of the lodge. Openings may be dug in upstream dams in winter in order to keep a passage open between the upstream pond and the lodge. Similar openings may also be made in dams downstream of the lodge. This may be necessary where water flow is reduced during winter due to freezing. Dam building is usually necessary where the water level is low or does not provide enough safe access to feeding areas. Beavers are very vulnerable to predation on land and rely on a quick escape to water to survive. Once the water levels are raised by a dam, beavers then have the luxury of being able to swim underwater undetected and they can also swim in and out of their lodges via the underwater entrances completely unseen. Deeper water also provides a large enough volume of water in which to create a winter store or cache of food and it also helps in the easier transport of large branches. Beavers may stop water levels getting too high in summer by digging a channel in the crest of the dam. They may also do this in winter if the water freezes over and the water level does not fall naturally as would be expected with reduced water flow. This creates a gap between the ice and water surface so that beavers may swim safely below the ice and still breathe. If the winter temperature rises above $-4°C$, the beavers may come out of the lodge to look for fresh food rather than relying on their winter store. They gnaw a hole through the ice and then tunnel through any snow to get to food. If the temperature is a bit lower, they tend to sit in the water under the ice or in the lodge while feeding, but if the temperature drops below $-6°C$, beavers will only brave the cold if they are really short of food.

Dams and lodges are normally built or renovated in the autumn, but summer building can occur if necessary. Ognev cites the example of a ditch occupied by beavers in the Komarin District of Belarus, which eventually became completely drained of water, thereby making it unsuitable for the resident beaver colony to stay there. In their frantic

A beaver carrying out maintenance work on a dam.

attempts to maintain the water level, the beavers built dams during the summer and dug a large series of burrows down the banks of the ditch as the water level continued to fall.

Dam building

The rate of dam building can vary greatly. For example, on Lake Osinka in Belarus, a 1.5-metre-long dam was built by Eurasian beavers overnight, but a 4-metre-long, 80-cm-wide, one–metre-high dam in Voronezh took 6 days and a 14-metre-long, 2-metre-wide dam in Norway took the beavers 21 days to build. In general Eurasian beavers do not usually build very big dams. It is unclear whether this is because they have a more reserved architectural style, or whether it reflects fundamental differences in the kind of water courses that the two species occupy. For example, in Belarus beaver dams were rarely more than eight metres long, but some exceptional dams have been recorded. The biggest dam recorded by Ognev in the Voronezh reserve in Russia was 120 metres long and up to 1 metre wide, but the largest on record from there was an awesome 170 metres long. North American beavers seem to be even more industrious and a dam more than 650 metres long, 7 metres wide and 4.3 metres tall was recorded on the Jefferson River, in Montana, USA.

The building of lodges may stimulate beavers to build dams in order to maintain water levels high enough for their lodges to remain moated. In general the males begin repairs to the larger leaks in dams in the autumn, but later all the colony members get involved. Females generally deal with the smaller leaks. Beavers use materials that have accumulated at the bottom of rivers or brooks, including branches and sticks that have been stripped of bark when the beavers were feeding.

The building of new dams always begins at the point (usually the narrowest) where the water makes the most noise when rushing past stones or some partial obstruction. From experiments on captive beavers,

A beaver drags a branch to a dam.

using tape recordings of rushing water, it is sound that stimulates beavers to begin building. Sounds in the wavelength range of 1000 to 2000 Hz have been shown to be optimal in stimulating dam building and these are commonly heard in rushing water. Beavers can often be seen turning their heads to the side to listen for the sound of rushing water to see if any further construction is required.

Therefore, beavers begin building dams when the acoustic stimuli are optimal. From experiments in captivity, it was found that the intensity of dam building rose with the rise in noise levels due to water rushing through heaped building materials. Once dam building is activated, the beavers continue to develop the dam even if the sound of the water is stopped. Dam building is stopped once the water level is great enough to allow for the creation of a winter cache (see p.68) and once the entrances to the lodge are submerged. However, if water levels drop for any reason, the winter store may become the site of a new dam; if water levels rise again the new dam may be converted once more to a cache. Dam building stops in winter once ice begins to form on the water.

If dam building is only weakly stimulated, mud and twigs are pushed against the source of the noise, but if strongly stimulated the beavers use coarser materials, which are unloaded in a random heap over the source of the sound, which is usually in depressions in the riverbed or in gaps in material already piled there. If large stones or rocks are present in the streambed, these may be pushed and lifted into place to create a wall, on which woody materials are placed.

When a beaver arrives at a dam with a load of building materials, it rises up on to its hind legs and walks bipedally up the steep downstream slope of the dam, carrying the material in its arms and under its chin. It then off loads the material on the upstream side of the dam

A beaver pins a branch into a dam.

just above the level of the water. In this way the height of the dam increases gradually along its entire length. As with lodge building, when the heap is roughly level, the beavers then start pinning smaller branches and finer material into any gaps and they also push and pack finer material on to the upstream side of the dam, in order to seal it and limit the flow of water through the incipient dam. However, unlike lodge building, the stimulus for this finer work is the sound of water trickling through the dam rather than just the visual stimulus of a gap or depression. As the dam becomes watertight, so the water level begins to rise on the upstream side. Further twigs and branches brought downstream by the water flow accumulate against the dam and are packed into the structure by the force of the water flow, contributing to the dam becoming watertight. Beavers seem to ignore leaks in the dam below the water surface, except when the water spurts through on the downstream side, which stimulates them to plug the gap with finer materials. However these repairs do not usually last long so that they have to be redone at regular intervals

Once the basic dam has been built, it is tightened up by packing finer material along the crest wherever water is pouring through. Beavers may use large branches and trunks to brace the dam. They drag them in the water to the crest of the dam and then, either floating in the water or by standing on the dam, they grip the branches with their incisors successively to edge them over the top of it. On the downstream side of the dam, the beavers push these larger branches into place usually at right angles to the crest of the dam, thereby supporting it from the bottom of the watercourse. Beavers may also use whole small trees, which are placed parallel to the water flow with the crown pointing upstream. The flow of water pushes the crown of the tree against the face of the dam and this helps contribute to the dam being watertight.

Beavers often excavate the stream bottom in front of the dam and use the mud to plaster it watertight. In its final form a dam has a gentle mud-covered upstream face leading to a hollow in the streambed, while there appears to be a more or less random assemblage of branches and twigs on the steep downstream face, which is supported by larger branches and small trees braced from the streambed or the banks. Obviously some water has to pass the dam and in the main this is via two channels at either end of the dam, where the beavers do not respond to the moderate sounds of running water by continuing to build the dam higher. By these very simple rules and techniques, beavers create what appears to the human eye to be a well-designed and well-constructed dam. And one that works.

Although young beavers join the rest of the group in dam building in their first winter at the tender age of 6-7 months old when all the motor actions associated with dam building are fully developed, they are not capable of making their own complete dam until their second autumn, because until then they do not respond to the appropriate stimuli.

Changing landscapes

Beavers are keystone species. This means that they have a major effect on shaping their environment, which also affects many if not all other species, with which they share that environment. The main river is a first order river and several tributaries may join it, termed 'second order rivers'. Each second order river may be fed by several streams, which are third order and so on. Beavers occupy second to fourth order rivers and streams, but their effects are similar in boreal ecosystems in Scandinavia and North America, where they impact on 20-40% of second to fifth order rivers and streams. The patches of land and water that are affected by a group of beavers vary greatly from only 0.5 to 30 hectares as recorded for North American beavers. Beavers may not only impact on large areas, but they may occupy sites continuously for 40 years or more, so their effects are not only profound but also long lasting, and may continue many years after they have abandoned a site. Clearly, building dams and cutting down trees affects many aspects of the riparian ecosystem. Most research on the effects of beavers on the landscape has been carried out on North American beavers and even then this has mostly applied to the effect that they have on the vegetation, particularly trees.

In general, once beavers have dammed a river or stream, the water level and water table both rise, and more anaerobic soil is created by flooding the neighbouring land. The dam slows the speed with which water flows downstream so that sediments carried by the flow settle on the riverbed. The rising water level kills any vegetation that is growing in soil if it cannot survive flooding. In particular, many tree species are prone to death owing to water-logged roots. Inevitably flood-intolerant species are replaced in due course by those that tolerate flooding. The plant succession following the arrival of beavers in an area depends on a number of factors, including water chemistry, soil type, silt depth and the amount of decaying vegetation in the water. However, if the vegetation is a floating mat in the water, the mat rises with the rising water level so that little change is evident except that the mat may now have an opportunity to expand in size as the surface area of the pond increases.

This occurred in Beckley Bog, in north-west Connecticut, USA, where over a thirty-year period tree cover reduced by two to five times as a result of flooding and felling, only to be replaced by a sedge-dominated open fen vegetation, which was better adapted to the wetter conditions.

1. Before colonisation by beavers.

2. Arrival of first pair of beavers.

3. *Changing land and water use.*

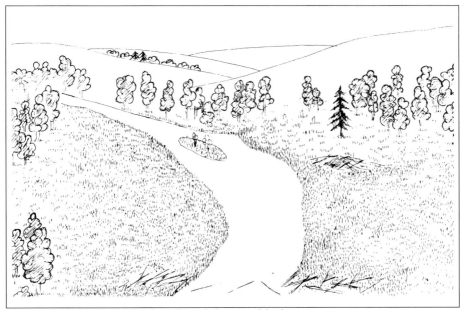

4. *Abandoned dam and lodge system.*

However, the open meadow, dwarf shrub and scrub shrub communities were unaffected. As expected, the floating mat of vegetation rose with water levels. More open water was also created for water lilies, which form an important food source for beavers throughout the year. Overall plant biodiversity was unaffected, but the species that grew in the bog were more adapted to wetter conditions.

Tree felling by beavers can reduce the amount of closed canopy forest and affect the composition of tree species growing there. Increased sunlight to the forest floor leads to more herbaceous vegetation, on which beavers feed in the summer months. Depending on whether beavers select aspen, willows or birches as their favourite foods, this can affect the way in which beavers are subsequently able to exploit the local vegetation. For example aspen resprouts as suckers from roots underground and can be slow-growing, but willows react rapidly and vigorously to coppicing.

One such study was carried out by Krister Jakobsson on the Pålböleån River in northern Sweden, which was colonised by Eurasian beavers in 1972. The riparian woodland was dominated by willows, which were also browsed by moose (*Alces alces*), mountain hares (*Lepus timidus*) and willow grouse (*Lagopus lagopus*). When studied in 1977-80 the total area supported about 100-200 European beavers, but there were only five lodges within the 1.4-km study site. Jakobsson went to great pains to look at the impact of beavers on the trees; a total of 1,369 trees were counted in the study area, most of which were closed-canopy downy birch (*Betula pubescens*) (1,039), with a few grey alders (*Alnus incana*) (144), Scots pine (*Pinus sylvestris*) (122), Norway spruce (*Picea abies*) (63) and a single willow. Jakobsson found that 433 or 92% of the trees (368 birches and 30 alders) that died in the study area up to 1980 were felled by beavers. The harvesting of trees selectively by beavers led to a dramatic change in the composition of the trees there: willows increased by 197%, grey alder by 13%, while downy birch fell by 6%. Moreover, the beavers tended to select birch trees with larger diameters (greater than 6.5 cm) within 10 metres of the bank, when they first colonised the area, but were forced to use small and then medium-sized trees as these became rarer. Finally, when resources fell too low, they were forced to travel further from the riverbank in order to find food.

However, beavers did not forage more than 30 metres from the river, even though there was plenty of birch more than 50 metres from the water. In another Swedish study beavers had travelled up to 125 metres from water in search of trees to fell, while in Finland 98% of the trees used by beavers were within 10 metres of the riverbank. Bushes on the Pålböleån River were mainly exploited within 5 metres of the bank, resulting in a decrease in willow bushes of 14% and an increase in birch bushes by 10%. Jakobsson concluded that despite some regeneration of birch, this was insufficient to support the current population so that the beaver groups would probably be forced to move on after another 10 to 15 years, because they were unwilling to forage further away from the water. Overall the deciduous forest closest to the river was affected most by the beavers with a significant decline in the size of trees over time.

The beavers do not always get it their own way. Moose and other deer can be major competitors for browse vegetation, including willows, which may contribute to local over-exploitation of food resources and affect the population density and breeding success of beavers.

In summary, beavers have the following direct effects on the ecosystem: they flood the land, increasing the area of open water and killing trees by waterlogging the roots or felling, which opens up the shoreline, and results in a net increase in aquatic or water-loving plants.

Beaver ponds may remain active and relatively stable for ten years or more at a time. In the Adirondacks and New York State beavers return to the same site after abandonment every 10 to 30 years, whereas in the mountains of Colorado, a cycle of two occupations and two abandonments was recorded over 70 years, with constant occupation for 30 years. In northern North America there is a complex pattern of ecosystem development, involving emergent marshes, bogs and forest wetlands, which appear to persist for centuries owing to the activities of beavers. Just what happens depends on the existing vegetation, the hydrology, topography, fires, diseases, and other herbivores as well as the beaver.

Beavers may have a long lasting effect beyond when they are resident. After dams have burst following lack of maintenance, the re-exposed land now covered in sediments is invaded by sedges and grasses. Sedges survive for longer on mud or peat than on well-draining sandy sediments, which are quickly invaded by shrubs and trees such as aspen and birch. Flooding may reduce the amount of mycorrhizal fungi in the soil, which may be important for the establishment of some tree species, thereby retarding their recolonisation. Even up to 12 years after beavers have left an area with only sparse willow and alder, there may be very little regeneration. Forest growth and regeneration may be reduced, because falling water levels result also in local droughts.

Finding food

Beavers have a very varied diet and are by no means restricted to a woody diet. In fact there is a distinct seasonality in their diet. During the later spring and summer they eat a wide variety of herbaceous plants on land and aquatic plants from the water, whereas in the autumn and winter the diet is dominated by bark from trees. In all beavers have been recorded feeding on 80 tree species and 149 others including herbaceous and aquatic species, although the actual number varies regionally.

The range of herbaceous plant species that beavers eat in summer is considerable. For example, in the Voronezh Reserve in Russia, the summer diet includes meadowsweet *(Filipendula ulmaria)*, nettles *(Urtica* spp.), angelica *(Angelica sylvestris)*, horse sorrel *(Rumex)*, water avens *(Geum rivale)*, thistles *(Cirsium heterophyllum)*, marsh marigolds *(Caltha palustris)*, mugwort *(Artemisia vulgaris)* (young leaves and shoots only), cattails *(Typha latifolia)*, reeds *(Phragmites)* and water lilies *(Nymphaea alba* and *Nuphar lutea)* (roots and subaquatic parts only). During the autumn, winter and first part of spring, they switch to fresh bark, the cambium of twigs, young shoots, the fine tips of branches, water lily roots, reeds, irises *(Iris pseudacorus)* and sweet flag *(Acorus calamus)*. Their favourite tree foods are aspen *(Populus* spp.), white willow *(Salix alba)*, and other willows, and bird cherry *(Prunus padus)*; birches *(Betula* spp.) and alder *(Alnus* spp.) are not eaten often, and maples *(Acer* spp.), oaks *(Quercus* spp.) and elms *(Ulmus* spp.) even less so. In all the beavers ate 148 out of the 560 available plant species on the Usmanka River flood plain in the Voronezh Reserve in Russia.

Beavers are renowned for cutting down trees (at 0.5-0.7 metres above the ground) and they certainly do feed on trees, and may cut down more than they need for a particular moment in time. This can make them less than popular with foresters and fruit growers, if they happen to choose the 'wrong' trees. Beavers eat the leaves and the finer twigs and sprigs of trees. In order of decreasing preference, beavers eat trees like aspen *(Populus* spp.), willows *(Salix* spp.*)*, rowan *(Sorbus aucuparia)*, birches *(Betula* spp.) and alder *(Alnus glutinosa)*. They also eat the bark from these trees, except for alder. Large alders are generally only used for building materials rather than food. Beavers eat only small amounts of the bark of pine *(Pinus* spp.) and spruce *(Larix* spp.), which they strip from the standing tree trunk as large conifers are usually not felled. Even

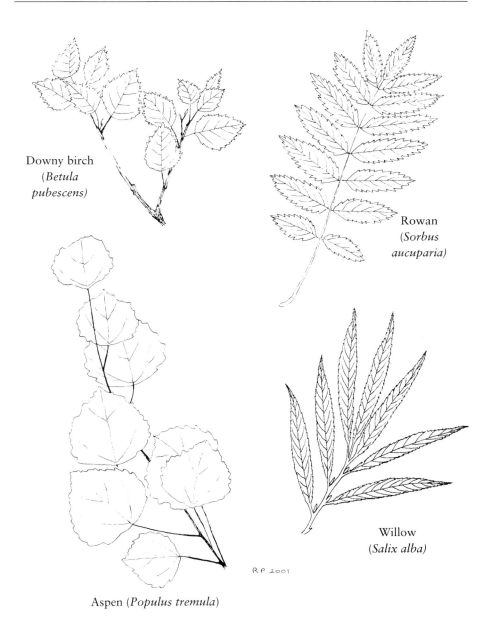

Downy birch
(*Betula pubescens*)

Rowan
(*Sorbus aucuparia*)

Aspen (*Populus tremula*)

Willow
(*Salix alba*)

RP 2001

Leaves of most popular trees eaten by beavers.

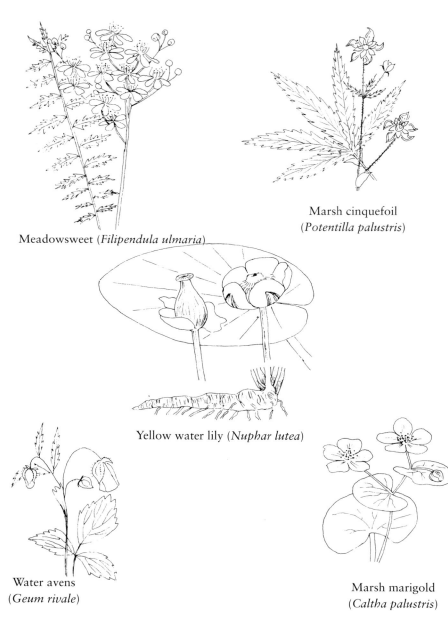

Meadowsweet (*Filipendula ulmaria*)

Marsh cinquefoil
(*Potentilla palustris*)

Yellow water lily (*Nuphar lutea*)

Water avens
(*Geum rivale*)

Marsh marigold
(*Caltha palustris*)

A selection of herbaceous and aquatic plants eaten by beavers in summer.

so beavers are not averse to peeling the bark and leaves off small twigs of spruce and fir trees. Beavers do not just eat any tree they happen to come across. They may sample trees by nibbling them before deciding whether to fell them or strip bark from them. For example, on the Pålböleån River in northern Sweden, the beavers sampled trees regularly (17% of all trees in the study area), especially where next to the river (65% of sampled trees). Most sampled trees were not subsequently felled and this was almost certainly because the levels of anti-herbivory toxins in the bark and leaves etc. were too high. These toxic chemicals are produced by plants to deter animals from feeding on them; they almost certainly do not taste very nice and would disrupt the metabolism of the animal if eaten in any quantity. North American beavers in Utah fed mainly on aspen bark, which was measured to have low phenol concentrations in 69% of cases,

Regional delicacies

Given its very wide geographical distribution, it is not surprising that the beaver's diet varies locally depending on what food is available. For example, in Russian Lapland in winter they rely mainly on downy birch (Betula pubescens) bark and twigs, and, to a lesser extent, willows. In summer they eat a variety of plants, but mostly grasses and the odd birch, including reed grass (Calamagrostis lanceolatus), sedges (Carex spp.), great willow herb (Epilobium angustifolium), thistles, marsh cinquefoil (Potentilla palustris), canary grass (Digraphis arundiancea), water avens, dropwort (Filipendula vulgaris) and goldenrod (Solidago virgaurea).

In northern Karelia in Russia most of the diet (97.5%) is birch, but there is very little in the way of alternatives, whereas in southern Karelia beavers are much more fortunate and willows make up most of the diet (53%) followed by aspen (21%) and bird cherry (12%).

Elbe beavers in Germany also concentrate mainly on aspen and willow, but they also vary their diet with elm, birch, cherry, hawthorn and hazel. Hazel is most often used when willows are not available in any particular area and is also the common winter food on the Danube.

compared with high concentrations in 75% of twigs. To put it in human terms, it is the difference between drinking a fresh cup of tea and a long-stewed cup of tea. The anti-herbivory tannins in the tea increase in concentration the longer it is left to stew in the pot, leading to a very unpleasant acrid taste. Although the juvenile stages of early successional trees like aspen and willow have toxic defence systems, they mostly escape browsing by growing very fast.

One tree is avoided at all costs despite having mineral-rich bark. Elder *(Sambucus nigra)* contains anti-herbivory compounds such as sambunigrin, which is a poisonous cyanogen glucoside, making it very unpleasant to feed on to say the least.

The selective foraging of reintroduced beavers in the Biesbosch of the Netherlands was also investigated. Most of the available trees were willows (96%), but the beavers selected the rarer species, including hazel, ash, aspen, cherry and alder. By varying their diet in this way, they are probably ensuring that they get a balanced diet. For example, hazel and ash are rich in sodium, whereas cherry and aspen have high levels of phosphorous. Mature aspen and aspen sprouts also have high levels of nitrogen, iron and zinc, whereas

RP 2001

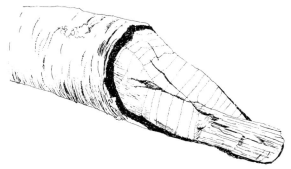

A beaver's distinctive tooth marks on a piece of birch wood.

calcium is high in aspen bark and magnesium is high in mature aspen twigs. If captive beavers are fed on a single tree species, they lose weight, showing that they need a variety of species to avoid dietary deficiencies. Unfortunately, the rarer species have just become rarer in the Biesbosch as the beavers have striven to get a well balanced diet.

By feeding on willows and hazel the beavers avoid eating secondary compounds with a high resin content, which make them unpleasant to eat. Birch leaves and bark have high levels of these secondary metabolites, which can cause a loss of sodium and behavioural stress, resulting from high potassium:sodium ratios. The Biesbosch beavers are particularly unfortunate as they are forced to feed on trees almost all year round; the few available aquatic plants and herbaceous species are unpalatable.

There are various estimates of how much food a beaver needs to eat each day. I am sure some of these estimates would horrify foresters, but much of what beavers eat is close to the river and involves much coppiced material as well as bark from trees. One estimate suggested that a beaver needs 7 kg of aspen per day, plus 2 kg of birch and 25 kg of willow. In other words a staggering total of more than four tonnes of woody vegetation and bark per year plus herbaceous and aquatic vegetation in the summer.

Collecting food

Beavers do not just chomp their way through the vegetation at hand, but they collect food together at different places along the river or pond bank. This gathered food is then transported along summer trails, which are the shortest routes back to the water. The beavers then swim to fixed feeding stations, which are usually situated at the edge of or in shallow water, so that they can easily dip their food into water and escape quickly into deeper water if necessary. Where the pond or river banks are quite low and flat, beavers usually fetch food from the side in the direction from which the wind is blowing, so that they can detect any approaching predators.

Felling trees

As we have seen at the end of the summer the beaver's diet changes from mainly herbaceous and aquatic vegetation to the bark of trees. A beaver gets access to most of its bark by felling trees. Tree felling generally only occurs during the autumn, but beavers may cut down trees in the winter and early spring if they can get above the ice and if the temperature remains above −4°C. However, tree felling mostly ceases by the time other vegetation is growing later in the spring.

There are various records of the maximum tree diameter felled by beavers. In Norway, the maximum recorded for a birch was 58.5 cm and for an aspen it was 68 cm, although for the oak, with its much harder wood, it was a mere 35 cm. In the Voronezh Reserve beavers fell willows and aspen up to one metre in diameter, but the biggest willow on record as having been felled by a beaver was a massive 106

Accidents will happen!

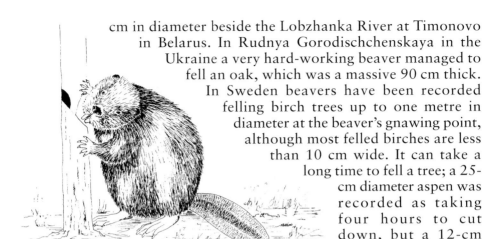

cm in diameter beside the Lobzhanka River at Timonovo in Belarus. In Rudnya Gorodischchenskaya in the Ukraine a very hard-working beaver managed to fell an oak, which was a massive 90 cm thick. In Sweden beavers have been recorded felling birch trees up to one metre in diameter at the beaver's gnawing point, although most felled birches are less than 10 cm wide. It can take a long time to fell a tree; a 25-cm diameter aspen was recorded as taking four hours to cut down, but a 12-cm tree took only half an hour. A willow of 80 cm in diameter in Voronezh took an incredible two years to fell.

Beavers do not plan where their trees are going to fall. Instead trees tend to fall in all directions, although those nearest to and beside the water tend to fall into the water, because this is the direction in which they are leaning and their crowns are more developed on the waterward side.

As with tunnelling, beavers prefer to gnaw alone at a tree. If a beaver comes across another one that is felling a tree, it will stop and groom itself before leaving. Temporarily defeated, the beaver may return later to see if the tree has been vacated.

When a beaver gnaws down a small tree or cuts up small branches and twigs, it bites against the grain, holding its head and the cutting edges of its incisors at about 135° to the length of the piece of wood. Thicker branches and tree trunks are also cut initially at a 135° angle by chipping a piece of wood and then tearing a strip away with its teeth. If this is not possible, the beaver laboriously chips away at the wood. The head is then turned through 90°, which means that it is held almost upside down when felling larger trees, in order to gnaw away at the other face of the cut. If the ground is fairly flat, the beaver works its way around the tree trunk resulting in two conical cut surfaces that meet at their apices.

Tree felling is exhausting work. Beavers gnaw away at a trunk for 5-10 minutes at a time and then rest, often panting heavily, and they also take the opportunity to sharpen their teeth, which must become rapidly

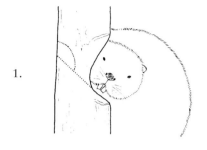

1. A beaver begins to gnaw at a tree at 135° to its length.

2. It turns its head almost upside down to gnaw at the upper part at 45° to the tree's length.

Tree felling.

blunt when used against all that wood. Now and then beavers break off from their hard work and go down to the water to have wash and a snack. However, beavers may work on a tree for up to one hour, if need be, and they can become so engrossed in their gnawing that it is possible to walk right up to them completely unnoticed. Gnawing at trees increases in intensity throughout the night from dusk and reaches a peak at around midnight, before decreasing again towards dawn. Beavers may also be very fussy when it comes to the quality of bark on a tree. Rough and scraggy bark may be left untouched for several nights before it is peeled off the trunk, and even then the beavers do this only half heartedly and sporadically. However, if a tree has fine bark and no branches low down on the trunk, the beavers do not fell the tree, but peel off the bark as high as they can reach.

When the tree trunk makes the slightest creak, signifying that it may be about to fall, the beaver jumps rapidly aside, so that it avoids being crushed by the falling tree. Beavers often look up just at this point and it has been suggested that they are looking for the direction in which a tree is about to fall. However there is no evidence to support this. If the tree is particularly large, the beaver rushes into the water as do any other beavers who may be nearby.

Once felled, if the trunk is too large to be moved, bark of good quality is peeled off and eaten on the spot. Any branches and tree trunks less than about 12 cm in diameter are cut up into manageable pieces that can easily be transported. At the feeding stations, beavers cut up the thicker branches and thinner trunks so that they can easily be handled while feeding. When transporting cut wood to water, beavers construct trails by digging and gnawing a clear path. This is often called road-building or canal-digging. These trails also make for a rapid escape if the beavers are suddenly surprised while collecting food. If the river bank is too steep, the beavers will dig out the bank until a trail of suitable gradient is

A beaver feeding on birch leaves.

produced. For example, on the River Faxälv in Sweden, beavers have dug deep furrows in steep banks from the level ground down to the water's edge. Once in the water beavers take their food to save for later use in the winter store or to a feeding station for immediate consumption.

Handling food

Beavers are very adept with their forepaws when looking for and manipulating food. Unlike other rodents, they do not use their noses and whiskers to feel for food, but they readily feel for food in the water using an outstretched forepaw. Having decided it is good to eat, the beaver first grasps it in one paw, lifts it to the mouth and then uses the other paw too to hold it while eating. The beaver's ability to manipulate food in its forepaws is probably more highly developed than in any other rodent. For example, young beavers bite the stalks from leaves, then roll the leaves together, using both hands, before eating them, rather like a pancake. By their second summer, they are able to take a sprig of leaves and delicately remove the leaves directly from the twigs.

When it comes to twigs and small sticks less than 5 mm in diameter, these are fed into the mouth end on and are steadily and quickly shredded with the incisors, rather in the way we eat bread sticks. Once a long piece has been fed into it mouth, a beaver stops and chews for a while before continuing. Very fine twigs are often bent double before being placed in the mouth. With bigger sticks, only the bark is eaten and the wood is discarded. Firstly, the beaver closely inspects the stick, drawing it back and forth in front of its nose and biting off any twigs and rough patches. If the bark is of good quality, the beaver grasps the stick in one hand, using its little finger as an opposable digit, or sometimes using both hands for shorter periods, and then it rotates the stick slowly and in a clockwise direction towards itself, while moving it sideways as it peels off the bark with its incisors.

If a branch is too big to be handled easily, then a beaver gets at the bark in one of two ways. Firstly, on felled wood it holds the palms of its forepaws against the branch as it gnaws away, rolling the branch as it does so, if it is possible. If the trunk is vertical, the bark is often easily removed by gnawing off the bark in long strips, which are peeled upwards and eaten piecemeal. Beavers do not like eating dry, hard bark, and so they carefully remove it in small pieces prior to tree felling.

A beaver gnawing bark from branches and twigs.

Gnawing and tooth sharpening

When a beaver is gnawing, its lower incisors cut mainly against the upper ones, which act as an anchor point against which the lower ones are able to bite. Obviously gnawing takes its toll on the sharpness of the incisors. Beavers stop frequently while tree felling or feeding to resharpen their dental blades using quick jaw movements as the teeth are ground against each other. To sharpen the upper incisors, a beaver uses the hard enamel of its lower incisors to cut away the softer dentine behind the enamel of the upper incisors. The lower incisors are sharpened in a similar way, by sliding the lower jaw slightly forwards so that the upper incisors can cut away behind the lower ones. This trimming action also keeps the enamel edge of the teeth sharp. In order to accommodate the huge amount of wear and tear that a beaver's incisors experience through heavy usage on wood, its incisors continue to grow throughout life so that it is always possible for a beaver to generate new, sharp cutting blades.

Drinking

Beavers do not lap up water using their tongues like many other mammals and they certainly do not use their tongues for grooming. When they are thirsty (and I imagine gnawing away at trees for hours on end is thirsty work), they simply hold their noses horizontally above the water surface and make chewing movements with their submerged mouths to suck in water.

Coecotrophy: a beaver eats its faeces.

'Not green faecal porridge again!'

Coecotrophy

Beavers have a very inefficient system for digesting cellulose, the primary nutrient available in vegetation. Experiments have shown that only about 30% of cellulose is digested when passing through their guts. Like all mammals, a beaver is unable to produce its own enzymes for digesting cellulose, but relies instead on microorganisms (mainly bacteria and protozoa) that live in its ceacum, which is part of the large intestine. The problem is that the hind gut has only a poor ability to absorb nutrients, hence the low digestive efficiency. In order to improve this situation, beavers produce a special kind of faeces, which looks like a green porridge, which they ingest, so that any nutrients not absorbed the first time around have an opportunity to be so the second time. This process is know as coecotrophy and occurs in other mammals, including notably the rabbit.

Beavers practice coecotrophy throughout the year. They produce the special faeces some time after they have been feeding, and sit on the ground with their tails pointing forwards so that they bend their noses down towards the anus, the edges of which they press with their forepaws while they noisily feed on these faeces. Coecotrophy only occurs on land, whereas normal defecation and also urination occur in the water unless used in scent-marking. Coecotrophy does not occur in young unweaned beavers that do not eat large quantities of solid food and young beavers have not been observed eating their mother's faeces either. It is not known how the young beavers develop their coecal flora to deal with cellulose.

Food stores

To ensure survival throughout the long winters, especially in northern latitudes, beavers create a store or cache of food, on which a beaver colony may be dependent for five to six months of the year. This consists of woody vegetation that is collected by all group members during the autumn and gathered underwater near the main entrance to the lodge. In the River Faxälv, in Sweden, the food stores were observed being located by the beavers in deep water with strong currents. Beavers use all the same behaviours used in the building of lodges and dams in order to collect and transport branches and twigs for the cache. The beavers construct the store by beginning at the lodge entrance and extending it into deeper water. Food caches are very compact and are built up from the bottom of the water course to the surface of the water. They are usually long and narrow in shape and curve in the direction of the current. Stores have commonly been recorded up to 10 metres long with a volume of around 80 cubic metres, but the largest on record was 15 metres long by 2.5 metres wide and 3.5 metres deep. They may comprise of, for example, willow branches 3-4 metres long sunk to a depth of 2-2.5 metres, which are rammed into the bank of the river by their sharp cut ends or which are laid loosely on top of each other. In Voronezh the beavers mostly store willow at first and also birch and cherry where it is abundant, but they also include oak, elm, aspen, roots of water lilies, marsh trefoils and cattails. In Belarus beavers have been recorded amassing stores of 10-25 cubic metres of almond willow plus roots of yellow water lily, water iris and manna grass *(Glyceria aquatica)*.

While much effort goes into the construction of main caches, those on tributaries are less well constructed because the water is usually much shallower and the current is less. However, not all winter food is necessarily stored this way. In the Ukraine beavers have been reported constructing store rooms within the lodge. If a beaver group is unfortunate enough to establish itself in a home range in the autumn, it starts to fell trees intensively in order to build dams and a lodge. However, if winter over takes them and there is not enough time to build an adequate cache for the duration of the winter, the beaver group may be forced to come out during milder weather to fell trees, but any aquatic vegetation surviving during the winter may also be an important extra source of food.

Beavers do not build winter caches unless they have to. For example, on the Rhone in France beavers can survive quite happily without building any dams, lodges or stores, but they can respond to more severe conditions if necessary. When Rhone beavers were translocated to Switzerland, they immediately began to create dams, lodges and, finally, stores in order to survive local conditions.

Beavers are probably stimulated to start building their winter stores by a number of factors, including falling temperatures, changes in food quality and their state of nutrition. In other words this occurs after they have changed from their summer to winter diets and after they have been busy for some time on other building activities. Food collecting also only begins if a group is very familiar with its home range and has already built a lodge. Beavers may collect food if there is no lodge, but never do so while working on the lodge, and even then they do not bring the food to a cache until other construction work is complete. It is during this period of the year when food is being collected that beavers may fell many coarser trees for their cache. By November the amount of food the beavers collect is decreasing, but their efforts are concentrated on high quality foods only. In Sweden the beavers continue to collect and store food until the rivers freeze over.

The tail as a larder

The tails of beavers are not only useful for helping them to swim, dive and warn of danger, but they act as fat stores. An analysis of 52 North American beaver tails showed that there was a seasonal change in tail volume. Tails became bigger from July to October, and thereafter they declined in volume. Further analysis showed that tails only increased in volume once they were 50% total fat. Beavers have two other major fat depots: the intraperitoneal (within the body cavity) and subcutaneous (under the skin) depots. Although the latter is more important (and no doubt helps insulate beavers from the cold in the water), it is the tail which is the primary site for fat storage and mobilisation.

Choosing foods

When it comes to choosing which trees to exploit for bark, twigs and leaves, beavers are fairly conservative, but as far as other vegetation is concerned, beavers learn to complement their diet with a wide variety of different plants. Young beavers often learn their dietary preferences by watching what their parents are eating, so that dietary traditions may become established in beaver groups. This example of social learning is undoubtedly of high adaptive value, since vegetation types may vary considerably throughout the beaver's wide geographical distribution. If beavers were to have an innate preference for only willow or aspen they would starve to death in areas dominated by birch. However, by learning from their parents, beavers are preadapted to whatever food is locally abundant.

Development of feeding

Observations on young beavers show that they are able to gnaw bark by the time they are only 4 days old, but they do not eat whole aspen leaves until 11 days old. By one month old beavers are virtually weaned, consuming mostly solid food and very little milk.

Young beavers do not remove leaves and twigs from branches when they first begin to feed on solids, but by twelve days old they attempt to hold a twig in their forepaws and only a few days later they are able to hold dandelion stems quite skilfully and adeptly. By one month old baby beavers are able to use their little fingers as opposable digits to grasp food items and by five weeks old they can squash leaves together into a ball for easier consumption. At 44 days old a young beaver was seen to grasp a leaf in one hand and bite off its stalk, before rolling the leaf or bending the stalks double so that they fitted better into its mouth.

At two months old young beavers have been seen rotating sticks and gnawing off the bark. By their first winter they are able to help construct and also get food from the winter store. Young beavers only make use of vertical trunks from which to strip bark, if fallen ones are not available.

Activity

Beavers are normally active by night and then sleep by day. In Russia peak activity during summer and autumn occurred between 9 in the evening and 1 in the morning, with a notable decline between 3 and 4 in the morning. In the Netherlands beavers during the winter left the lodge at about 6 in the evening, returning at about 6 in the morning, a full twelve-hour shift, whereas in summer they did not leave until almost 8 in the evening and returned before 6 in the morning, so that they were active for a full two hours per day less. In areas where they are not persecuted, beavers may also come out during the day. When inactive, they sleep in the sleeping chambers in the lodges either stretched out on their sides or on their backs, or lying on their bellies with tails tucked up underneath their bodies. Beavers often yawn when they are tired, but they have never been seen to stretch.

Movements and dispersal

At about two years of age, young beavers often travel along rivers and streams during the floods in the spring and early summer when dispersing from their home lodge, but they have also been recorded moving between different water courses. Their journeys are usually less than 20 km but they may journey up to 100 km through wooded mountainous country. On the River Elbe, beavers disperse on average about 26 km, whereas in Switzerland dispersal distances are typically 10-20 km, although the most adventurous ventured up to a maximum of 120 km. A North American beaver, which escaped from a private collection at the south end of Loch Lomond in Scotland, was eventually run over by a lorry almost 40 km to the north.

A bad fur day

It is essential that beavers take good care of their fur, because they rely on its water repellence and insulating properties to keep warm while swimming and also during long, cold winters. If the fur becomes soiled or sticky, it loses its water repellence and would quickly become waterlogged, if it entered the water. Both wetness and dirt trigger a beaver to start grooming. Beavers appear to use anal gland secretion to help waterproof their fur; when deprived of their anal glands, they apparently soon become waterlogged.

After its first dip of the evening, a beaver emerges from the water on to land or into the lodge, and begins to shake, starting from the head and moving along to the rear of the body; it then begins to groom and clean itself thoroughly and at great length, at first using its forepaws. Grooming is repeated several times during the night, usually on land, but shy beavers retreat to the lodge for their ablutions.

There is a strict sequence of grooming movements and the description below is typical of that used by all beavers. A beaver begins its wash and brush up by cleaning its nose and head using its forepaws. If its nose is dirty, it sneezes and cleans its nose intensively, using quick simultaneous movements of its hands. When it comes to the fur, it clenches its hands

A beaver grooms itself thoroughly with its hands.

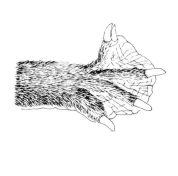

A beaver grooms itself with the special double claw on the hind foot.

together loosely with its thumbs pressed against the fur and then draws its hands from back to front against the lie of the fur. Starting at its nose the beaver works backwards to behind its ears. The belly fur gets the greatest attention and the claws are used to comb from the mid-line outwards at the same time, drawn at an oblique angle to they way in which the fur lies. It then combs its forelegs either with or against the fur and then switches to its hind legs, combing against the fur with either one or two hands. Finally, the beaver grooms its rear flanks and back with one forepaw by stretching backwards and drawing it against or across the fur. Therefore, a beaver uses its forepaws to groom all parts of the body within easy reach.

The head, the forearms and the foremost part of the body may also be reached using the hind legs and this kind of grooming is usually stimulated by a skin irritation. To help with grooming, the second digits on their hind feet have a double claw, which acts like a comb to help maintain the fur. The hind foot is raised and the second toe is inclined to the side, so that it is at right angles to the rest of the toes, and then it is applied to the area of fur that needs to be cleaned. The beaver bends its toes slightly, so that the double claw opens up. Then the foot is lowered and the double claw is drawn through the fur like a comb with the toe stretched, while the others are bent tightly away from the fur. The claw is then closed and the whole sequence begins again.

Beavers groom their underfur using their incisors, which make small quick movements. This is sometimes done while cleaning the fur with the hands, but often it is done in response to a skin irritation. The belly, back, legs and rear flanks are all groomed by the teeth; to do this the beaver grabs some skin in its forepaws and stretches it so that it concentrates its grooming to a specific area.

Despite the use of legs and the incisors, beavers cannot reach all parts of their bodies. All members of a beaver group must indulge in mutual grooming if they are to retain overall water repellent fur. Mutual grooming tends to be concentrated on those parts of the body that cannot be reached on their own, including especially the middles of their backs and napes of necks. Mutual grooming also serves a social function, as it helps reinforce group cohesion throughout a beaver's life.Even more importantly, young beavers do not know how to groom and would risk hypothermia every time they entered the water. Not surprisingly mother beavers groom their babies intensively, so that their youngsters' fur remains water repellent.

Grooming actions seem to be largely innate, but it takes a while for young beavers to be good at grooming. Baby beavers may attempt grooming at only four days old after they have had their first dip in the water within the lodge. Although successful at grooming their noses and muzzles with their forepaws, and using the double claw on their hind feet to groom their flanks with fully developed behaviour, they often fall over backwards as they attempt to comb their bellies. By 12 days old young beavers are well able to hand groom behind their ears and can now reach their chin and bellies with their hind feet. By 19 days old they can sit up and successfully groom their bellies so that at this very early age all grooming behaviour is fully developed.

Scent-marking and territories

As for most mammals, scent-marking provides an important way of communicating with other members of the group and also with those from outside the group. What is communicated is not always clear to us and this is especially the case with the beaver. One of the most important functions of scent-marking is to indicate to other beavers which animals are resident in a particular area. Beavers are well endowed with scent glands and their secretions.

Scent glands and castor sacs

Both males and females have three sets of scent-producing organs. The pedal glands are found on the soles of the feet, the paired anal glands are found inside the cloaca, as are the paired castor sacs, which are often incorrectly called preputial glands, because they open into the urethra.

The anal glands are surrounded by a muscular sheath. Each anal gland opens independently into the cloaca via a papilla, which bears a few short, stiff hairs. Contraction of the muscular sheath forces the gland contents out via the papillae, which are protruded from the cloaca. The smell of the secretions from scent glands are often modified by their own bacteria, but it is not known whether beaver anal gland secretion is affected this way. Two bacteria species are common in the anal glands of North American beavers: *Escherichia coli* is an aerobic species common in the guts of mammals including people, and *Bacterioides fragilis* is an anaerobic species common in the guts of rodents. The anal gland secretion has a heavy pungent smell and its colouration varies according to the sex and species of beaver. Although in both sexes it contains a high proportion of lipids (fats or oils), the chemical composition of anal gland secretion is very different for the two sexes. The significance of these differences is unknown. Anal gland secretion is not only used in scent-marking to provide an 'identity card' for its owner when spread on the fur, but it is said also to be responsible for waterproofing the fur, although recent research disputes this.

The castor sacs are simple, thin-walled, sack-like extensions opening into the urethra, which leads from the bladder to the cloaca. A thin internal lining of cells produces a yellowish substance, which rapidly turns brown when exposed to sunlight and air. The castor sacs are not glands (like the anal glands), because castoreum is created when urine is flushed through them, so that it mixes with the castor sac secretion. Both anal glands and castor sacs are proportional in size to overall body size; in the case of castor sacs, being 0.9-1.2% (155-240 g.) of body weight in adults. Castoreum is first produced at three months of age, but the castor sacs are relatively much smaller than in adults; only 0.4% of body weight in the first autumn to spring. Castor sacs reach adult size by their third spring when they are two years old.

It has been suggested that the anal gland secretion and castoreum communicate in different ways. Being of low molecular weight, the volatile castoreum is readily and widely dispersed and can therefore possibly be detected far from where the scent-mark is made, but is not long lasting. However, the high molecular weight anal gland secretion is only detected at close range, but is likely to be longer lasting.

Castoreum

Castoreum from North American beavers has been analysed and found to contain 45 different substances, which include alcohols, phenols, ketones, aromatic carboxylic acids, esters, salicylaldehyde and castoramine. In other words, it consists of low volatile metabolites of urine and also includes other compounds secreted by the castor sacs. Castoramine ($C_{15}H_{23}O_2$) is a very pungent and highly volatile alkaloid, giving beavers their distinctive smell. A piece of castoreum I sniffed recently had an aromatic smoky smell. Other chemicals found in the castor sacs (but not in urine) include *cis*-cyclohexane-1,2-diol and two yellow pigments. However, these three compounds can be made from urine products when urine is flushed into the castor sacs, whereas castoramine cannot and must be produced directly by the cells lining the castor sacs. In many mammals the distinctive smell of the scent gland secretion is created by a distinctive flora of bacteria, which modify the secretion. This is not the case in the beaver's castor sacs.

The medicinal properties of castoreum have been likened to aspirin. Castoreum contains salicin (also known as α-2 dihydroxyglucoside of toluene, $CH_2OHC_6H_4OC_6H_{11}O_5$) or also saligenin-α, D-glucoside, whereas aspirin contains acetylsalicylic acid ($CH_3COOC_6H_4COOH$). Salicin has similar properties to aspirin as an antipyretic to reduce raised body temperatures and as an analgesic to relieve pain. Therefore, beavers have been hunted so relentlessly in the past for the very real medicinal properties

Depositing castoreum.

of their castoreum. Beavers obtain their salicin from the bark of willow trees and then concentrate it before eliminating it via the castor sacs.

Scent-marking

Beavers scent-mark with their anal glands by dragging the cloaca along the object being scent-marked, with the anal glands protruding from the cloaca. The tail is held horizontal and rigid, and is drawn across the scent mound afterwards. It is possible that anal gland secretion may be mixed with castoreum when it is being deposited, although anal glands are not used for scent-marking during the winter. Castoreum is sprayed on to piles of earth, snow, tree trunks or other protruding objects. To do this, the beaver arches its back with its body held over the object to be marked. The cloaca is forced out so that the papillae that are the openings to the anal glands are protruded. It then sprays the castoreum, while scratching itself with one hind leg, which helps spread the castoreum around. Before it leaves the scent-mark, the protruding cloaca is brushed against the marked object. Sometimes a beaver will just evert its cloaca and press it against a previous scent-mark. In a colony of beavers this may help create a group scent by sharing bacteria, which helps group members recognise each other. Beavers may also spray castoreum on to their feet and anal gland secretion is probably applied to the tail when scent-marking so that their scent is spread along trails.

Scent mounds

Beavers mostly spray their castoreum on scent mounds or sign places. These are created by scratching up piles of earth, snow, twigs and sticks to a height of 10 cm and a width of 15 cm; the largest on record are more than one metre high and 30 cm in diameter. They are usually constructed by the water or higher up the bank and because they are used so frequently, there are often well-trodden trails leading to and from them. Each colony may have up to 38 scent mounds and these are found mostly towards or at the edge of the group's home range. In some cases scent mounds are found in association with lodges, feeding and resting places and trails. Beavers mark their scent mounds regularly and it is possible that all group members mark their scent mounds every day. Scent-marking is often triggered by a strange odour or the scent-mark of a strange beaver on the scent mound. When beavers encounter these strange scent-marks, they hiss loudly, sniff the mound, slap their tails or over mark with their own scent-mark. In Russia females have been observed rubbing their bellies over existing scent-marks, when in oestrus. Beavers can sex other beavers from their scent-marks, and even identify individuals.

Although beaver groups tend to avoid each other's home ranges, scent-marks do not keep them away. Indeed, on the River Faxälv in Sweden, beavers from different groups were observed to have a common feeding area, where they were indifferent to each other's presence, but they would return to their respective lodge areas during the night to scent-mark around these and they would leave their final scent-marks there as they returned to their lodges in the morning. This is not unusual in mammals and it was not until recently that we began to understand how these scent-marks function. Rather than creating a barbed wire or electrified fence to prevent the entry of all strange beavers, scent-marks provide vital information as to whether area is being used by a beaver group and how to identify them.

Beavers do indeed mark themselves when spraying castoreum and depositing anal gland secretion, and they do sniff and over mark the scent-marks of other beaver groups. Indeed, neighbouring groups may share a scent mound, by both marking it. Both sexes deposit castoreum, checking scent-marks and overmarking if necessary. However, females do not spray castoreum on scent mounds when they have young, but they do so intensively just before they give birth and also begin again in the autumn once the young are able to look after themselves.

Scent mounds are only built during the summer, from April to June, with lower activity from July to October and least during the winter (October to March), when the group tends to be confined to the lodge. Frank Rosell and Bart Nolet have investigated in detail the territorial function of scent-marking in Eurasian beavers. They found that a beaver group scent-marked more often when living close to other beaver territories compared with isolated groups, and that the number of scent-marks increased with the number of neighbouring territories and individuals, the length of occupancy of the territory, and the length of wooded river bank in the territory. However, scent-marking frequency was not related to the number of animals in a group, or the ages of the animals. The number of scent mounds produced by a beaver group is not affected by whether the group is breeding or not, but by the number of neighbours, and there were no seasonal differences in the number of scent-marks during the summer. Therefore, scent-marking clearly has a territorial function.

Rosell and his colleagues also investigated scent-marking throughout the year at the River Bø in Norway. They found that beavers produced more scent-marks during the spring (April-May), when subadults are dispersing. The scent-marks were also found to be concentrated upstream towards the boundaries of territories, thus suggesting that they play an important role in defining the territory for residents and intruders alike. The flow of water may spread the scent throughout the beavers' territory.

Scent mounds are not usually built near the lodge, although there is occasionally one, but even so it is usually more than 600 metres away. If an artificial scent mound with castoreum from a strange male is built within the territory of a beaver group, the residents respond to the strange scent by over marking in 80% of cases. However, if an artificial scent mound is placed close to an inhabited lodge, the inhabitants may move on after apparently finding themselves suddenly in the home range of a strange beaver group. Beavers can also be enterprising. If they find an unoccupied lodge with no active scent mounds, they may well take over the lodge and home range. The scent-marks affect the emotional state of a beaver, mainly by increasing the confidence of residents and the anxiety of intruders.

At only two months of age, young beavers show characteristic castoreum-spraying behaviour, even though they are unable to produce any castoreum until they are at least five months old. Beavers start to deposit castoreum in earnest, when they leave their natal group at about two years old.

Friend or foe?

Morris Gosling of the University of Newcastle first proposed the scent-matching hypothesis for how scent-marks work based on his studies of African antelopes. However, it seems that this hypothesis is also applicable to the scent-marking of many other mammals, including beavers.

Scent-matching works on the basic principle that mammals can recognise and discriminate between their own and others' scent-marks. During the scent-marking process some of the scent is spread deliberately or accidentally on to the animal's body thus giving it the same smell as its scent-marks. When an animal enters the home range of a strange animal, it sniffs the existing scent-marks (and often scent-marks over them, although not in the case of beavers) so that it gets an idea of who might be at home and how long since they were there. If the interloper comes across an animal in the strange territory, it can then compare the smell of the scent-marks it has encountered with the smell of the animal in front of it, and in this way it can determine whether it is one of the home range owners or not. On the basis of this information, it can then decide whether to continue on its way, fight the animal or run away, which is the most likely scenario if the encountered animal is one of the home range owners.

Making a quick escape

Being large and slow-moving on land, beavers represent an ideal meal for large carnivores. Among the known mammalian predators of adult beavers are wolves (*Canis lupus)*, foxes (*Vulpes vulpes)* (which kill kits), brown bears (*Ursus arctos*), wolverines (*Gulo gulo*) and lynx *(Lynx lynx)*. Otters (*Lutra lutra*) have been known to predate kits by swimming into lodges and similar predation has been recorded by American mink (*Mustela vison*), in North America. Presumably introduced mink in Europe could also prey on Eurasian beaver kits where they occur in the same region. Foxes (*Vulpes vulpes)*, may share the burrow system of beavers, but do not make very good tenants, because they are known to kill beaver kits. However, most of these predators have only a minimal effect on beaver populations. Two major exceptions are humans (see p.119) and the wolf. Wolf predation may be very severe where their normal ungulate prey base has been eroded by, for example, human hunting.

Other recorded predators of beavers include eagles (*Aquila* spp.), sea eagles (*Haliaeetus albicilla),* goshawks (*Accipiter gentilis*), buzzards (*Buteo buteo*), tawny owls (*Strix aluco)* and the pike (*Esox lucius).*

So paranoid are beavers of being eaten that they are easily put off their food by the odours of their predators. Frank Rosell and Andrzej Czech dipped aspen sticks into human sweat and the faeces of foxes, otters, lynxes, wolves, brown bears and dogs to see what effect this would have on the feeding of beavers on the sticks. All of these odours significantly reduced beaver feeding during the summer, with the exception of human sweat and dogs. However, in the autumn, only otter, lynx, fox and human odours reduced beaver feeding. Surprisingly, otter odour had the most effect on beaver foraging, but Rosell and Czech conclude that this is not because the otter is a significant predator, but because they may find otter faeces particularly unpleasant.

As a result of all these opportunistic predators, beavers are very nervous of being on land and rush to the water at the slightest alarm. They rely on water as their main protection against all these predators. By damming rivers and creating large expanses of water, they minimise the distance they have to flee. Canals also help in this way. Lodge and burrow entrances are usually below water, so that beavers can come and go from their homes unseen. If a beaver is disturbed in its lodge, it can sneak out

White-railed eagle
(*Haliaeetus albicilla*)

Brown bear
(*Ursus arctos*)

Human
(*Homo sapiens*)

Lynx
(*Lynx lynx*)

Wolf (*Canis lupus*)

Fox
(*Vulpes vulpes*)

Beaver family in water

Wolverine
(*Gulo gulo*)

Otter (*Lutra lutra*)

Mink (*Mustela vison*)

Pike (*Esox lucius*)

Predators of beavers.

unnoticed and swim undetected for up to 800 metres away underwater before it needs to surface and breathe.

If the worst case scenario arises and a beaver becomes trapped on land, it flattens itself against the ground and remains still. Similar behaviour has been observed in other rodents. Beavers squat in this way at the bottom of water courses in order to avoid predators too. If a determined predator continues to approach the stranded beaver, it may hiss loudly or make a mock attack by charging at the assailant and pushing it with its nose. Beavers only bite after intense provocation.

They sense danger either mostly by sight or by smell. In the water, beavers sniff while raising their noses up and down rhythmically. They do a similar thing on land, except they hold their bodies in a more or less upright position.

When swimming in the water and usually after being alerted by strange scents or noises, just about anything that moves stimulates a beaver to slap its tail against the surface of the water before diving. This makes a big noisy splash. Beavers slap their tails usually when there is no immediate danger, but where a threat is suspected. Other members of a group respond differently to tail slapping according to where they are at the time. If they are on the land, they rush back to the water as quickly as possible. If they are in shallow water they swim immediately out into deep water, but if they are in deep water already they sniff the air and do not dive until they can also sense a dangerous sight, sound or smell.

Sometimes danger threatens immediately, and in this case a beaver dives without slapping its tail. Often the scared beaver resurfaces at a distance with only its eyes and nose above water, where it waits motionless to determine the real nature of the danger.

On land an anxious or excited beaver may strike its flat tail on the ground and alarmed animals often walk along with their tails held raised, so that they are ready to tail slap at any moment. If they are surprised near water, or on open paths or in tunnels, they may try to deter predators by rushing forward and slapping their tails on the ground.

Young beavers need to be taught which species are potential predators and so remain quietly within the lodge until their flight responses are fully and appropriately developed. At only a day old beavers are able to hiss loudly and leap out of the way of predators which may get into the lodge and by a week old they can turn about too, sometimes turning over completely in their attempts to get away. By ten days old they are able to seek protection in the water and they also dive when disturbed, and by

Beaver tail slapping to warn a predator that it has been seen.

one month old they start to slap their tails on the water surface before diving. From this time on young beavers are really shy and they become even more shy as young adults when they begin to spend whole nights outside the lodge foraging. At two months of age young beavers are able to squat on the bottom of the river or pond for up to 15 minutes waiting for danger to pass by. Young beavers may respond to a wide variety of different and non-dangerous stimuli and its takes until their second spring for them to learn to respond to the real dangers of life.

Social groups

The basic beaver social group consists of an adult breeding pair with up to two litters from the current year and the previous year. A study of the numbers of North American beavers per lodge in Michigan, USA, found an average 5.1 beavers with a maximum of 14 in the 57 lodges that were examined. Beaver numbers may be affected by the kind of food trees that are available. For example, in the Rocky Mountains in areas rich in aspen, the mean number of beavers was 7.8 in five lodges, compared with a mean of only 5.1 in seven lodges in areas of willow lacking any aspen. The maximum number of beavers recorded in a lodge was 18.

On the River Faxälv in Sweden the numbers of beavers per lodge conformed to the expected norm, but between two and four adult males and a similar number of non-breeding adult females were found near the same lodge, which indicated that in the summer at least, non-breeding animals commonly wander within the defended range of a breeding beaver group.

Each year only a single litter of beaver kits is born and the adult male is usually driven out of the lodge shortly before they are born. The male may or may not remain in the vicinity of the lodge during the summer and lives in a temporary den until the autumn. If the male stays nearby he may start bringing food to the female only three days after the birth of the litter. In captivity the situation may be quite different. Observations of a North American beaver group at Zurich Zoo in Switzerland showed that not only the male, but also young from the previous year, remained in the lodge and helped in the rearing of the young. Both the female and the male ate the placenta. Perhaps the lack of any competitors and a guaranteed and rich food supply allows for this highly integrated family life. Certainly on the River Faxälv in Sweden only the female and her young remained in the lodge during the summer. The rest of the group foraged often farther afield until September, when the colony as a whole began again the annual tasks of building and repairing lodges and dams and collecting food for the winter cache. However, on the main river where food supplies remain good throughout the year, the rest of the group also remained near the lodge throughout the summer. The group cohesion was maintained during nocturnal foraging when group members met and groomed each other frequently.

When they are two years old, young beavers usually leave their home lodge and set up home somewhere near the family residence. However, if a yearling beaver is separated from or loses its mother, it may pair up in the spring and defend a new territory, but these yearlings never breed until the spring of their second year. Yearling beavers may also disperse in low density populations where there is little

competition for territories. Even when yearlings pair up and become territorial like this without losing their mothers, they often return to their natal group in the autumn. Even two year olds will do this, which explains why some beaver groups become very large in winter. The benefit of this is the nice warm temperature in the lodge and help with foraging for food. Many beaver hands make light work in the reconstruction and maintenance period and while food stores are accumulated. Even so, never more than 18 beavers have been recorded in a single lodge.

Sexing beavers

Male and female beavers are about the same size and both have a cloaca that is closed tight by a sphincter, so that the only other external difference between the sexes is the prominent nipples in lactating females. The problem of sexing beavers has certainly exercised the minds of people attempting beaver reintroductions. One method for determining sex is to radiograph each beaver in an attempt to pick up the penis bone or baculum of the males. It is also possible to palpate for the baculum, but this requires a lot of cooperation from the beaver. Another method, which was developed recently by Frank Rosell and Lixing Sun, relies on differences in the colouration of the anal gland secretion of males and females. In males the anal gland secretion is oily, pale straw to whitish in colour and has a stronger and different smell to the pasty, grey, unpleasant-smelling secretion of females. This technique also differentiates between the two beaver species.

Females tend to be a bit heavier than males on average. On the River Faxälv in Sweden 26 males had a mean weight of 19.5 kg compared to 26 of their slightly more portly partners who weighed a mean of 20.1 kg.

Rather bizarrely, beaver males have a *uterus masculinus* (male uterus), which is well-developed in Eurasian beavers, but which is variably

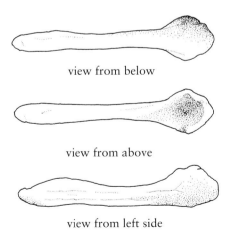

view from below

view from above

view from left side

The penis bone or baculum of a Eurasian beaver.

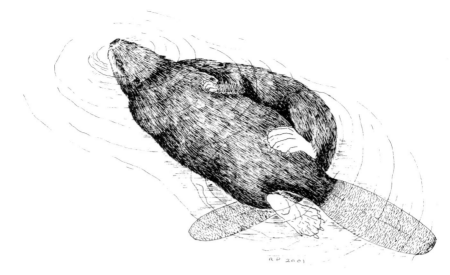

Mating beavers.

developed and sometimes absent in North American animals. The *uterus masculinus* has a similar cellular structure to the female uterus, but is not as well developed. There are cyclic changes in the *uterus masculinus*; as the male comes into breeding condition, so the epithelial and gland epithelial cells of the *uterus masculinus* decrease in height. The reason why beavers have this structure is unknown.

Reproduction

In any year most adult females can expect to breed; for example 89% on the River Faxälv. Of 11 pregnant or lactating beavers found on the River Faxälv, only one animal was a subadult of possibly two years old. Female beavers generally only reach sexual maturity at 18 months to two years old, and few have established a territory at this tender age, which explains the lower percentage breeding. Although young females breed at first in their second year, high population densities, slow growth rates and inhibition by older dominant females may cause this to be delayed.

On the Vorozhnev Reserve, some interesting differences in breeding were noted between the two beaver species. Whereas Eurasian beavers mate in January, North American beavers on the same site tended to mate one month later in February. Courting beavers were often seen to

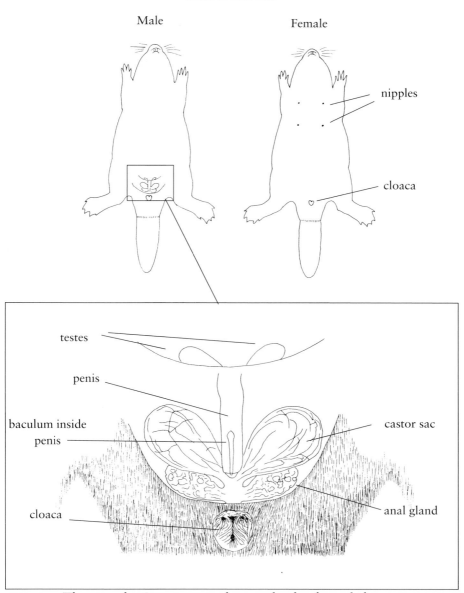

SEXING BEAVERS.

Male

Female

nipples

cloaca

testes

penis

baculum inside penis

castor sac

cloaca

anal gland

The reproductive organs and scent glands of a male beaver.

sniff, rub against and over mark scent-marks. The male attempts to mount the female 1-2 days before the actual mating occurs and the courting couple often sit near each other and mutually groom, emerge earlier than usual on the day of mating, chase after each other before diving into water and returning to lodge. The male mounts the female many times, but they copulate successfully only 3-4 times. During mating on land the female adopts the mating position by sitting on her forelegs and raising her tail and rear end towards the male. Beavers often mate in the water; a copulating couple of North American beavers were seen with the female lying flat on the surface of the water and the male clinging to one of her flanks so that their tails met at right angles thereby enabling their cloacae to meet. Similar behaviour was observed on land or in water in the Voronezh Reserve in Russia; the male clasps the female above the hips with his forearms and turns on his side, hanging on while the female swims around slowly for a short time. They then churn in the water and dive with a splash, before coming to the surface, swimming to the shore and repeating the whole process again with the female leading. On the River Faxälv in Sweden, mating took place either in the lodge or under the ice during the winter. With all these fieldworkers snooping around who can blame them for wanting some privacy?

Female beavers are 'seasonally polyoestrous', meaning that each year a female may have 2-4 oestrous cycles during the spring, which last about 7-15 days each. Females remain in oestrus (i.e. they are receptive) for about 10-12 hours and if they do not mate successfully, they come into oestrus again some two weeks later. If mating is successful, the gestation period is an average of 105 days (range 103-108 days) for Eurasian beavers compared with a mean of 107 days for the North American species (range 104 to 111 days). In other words there is no significant difference in gestation period between the two species. On the River Faxälv the kits are born at the end of May or the beginning of June after the disruptive spring period, when ice breaks up and melts cause flooding, and younger beavers have finished dispersing.

Litter size

After labour lasting for up to nine hours, Eurasian beavers may have litters of between 1 and 5 kits, but 2 or 3 is the usual number. On the River Faxälv the normal litter size was usually 1, with only one case of 3 and two of 4 known. It has been suggested that some populations have smaller litter sizes because in northern latitudes the beaver group is almost entirely dependent on the winter cache for up to six months of the year.

North American beavers appear to be much more productive than their Old World cousins. Examining the numbers of foetuses or placental scars found in hunted animals revealed that even some subadults had litter sizes of up to 3 in a sample of seven individuals. Adults were even more productive with litter sizes up to 6 in a sample of 34 animals. However, these numbers may not represent live births; there was evidence for resorption of at least one foetus in 27% of females that were examined. As with the Eurasian beaver, litter size varied with food availability and height above sea-level. Litter size was greater in areas with an abundance of food trees such as aspen or willows and at 2,500 metres elevation they were about half of those at elevations 1,000 metres below, even though food was abundant. Ovulation rate also increased with age, reaching a plateau at about 4-5 years old.

When they are born, beaver kits weigh 300 to 700 g each. They have incisor teeth partly erupted (3 mm long) and their eyes are partly open, but by day two to three they are fully opened. As with all mammals, the first milk is called colostrum and contains antibodies, which help the kits resist diseases for the first few weeks of life until they can begin to produce their own. At about one month old the mother's nipples begin to shrink suggesting less lactation. By this time the premolars have erupted and all molars are present at 5.5 months, but even so the kits are usually fully weaned by about two to three months old at about the end of July, when they begin to investigate their surroundings outside the lodge and even fetch their own food. Young beavers may be reluctant to leave the lodge, especially if they have to leave earlier than two months old. Before they can move outside the lodge, the young are dependent on the male, female and older siblings to carry food into the lodge for them. At only one week old, kits begin to eat solid foods, which is similar to the very precocious development seen in many other rodent species. The milk teeth are usually fully replaced by the permanent dentition in February or March of the following year when they are about ten months old.

The development of beaver kits may be further accelerated if older animals within the group leave for some reason (usually a disaster); this may force kits to leave the lodge in search of food as young as only two weeks old. Flooding of the lodge in spring and early summer may also result in an early evacuation to a temporary nest until the young are able to go outside.

Beaver kits suckling.

Suckling

During the first 24 hours after their birth, the mother beaver lies almost constantly with her young, leaving only briefly a few times to feed and bathe. Thereafter during the daytime the mother allows almost unrestricted suckling by her kits, except when she grooms them. At night, she only comes to them to suckle a few times and she spends most of the time out in the water feeding and bathing.

Beaver kits suckle frequently and irregularly and they certainly do not suckle all at once. A suckling bout usually lasts for about five to ten minutes, but may go on for up to half an hour or more. Like other mammals beaver kits knead with their forepaws to encourage let down of milk. After a good feed they may even fall asleep on the nipple.

Most milk is produced by the lower pair of nipples; the upper pair produce only 50-75% as much and these nipples are not normally used if litters consist of only one or two young. Most milk is produced between

20 and 70 days after birth and more milk is produced for larger litters. Mothers go on producing milk for 90 days, even though the kits start taking substantial solids at only 30 days old. For the first three to four days, beaver kits need 65-70 g/day, which rises rapidly to an average of 107 g/day for the next 8-9 days, eventually reaching a maximum of 128 g/day.

Apart from its antibody load, colostrum has more than double the level of lactose of normal milk. Normal beaver milk has a very high fat (mean 18.2%), protein (11.4%) and dry matter (32.8%) content compared with the milk of many other mammals. Beaver milk has four times the fat and twice the albumin of cow's milk. During lactation concentrations of the milk components increases, although towards the end of the period there is a decline, so that milk composition is similar to that on day 10 after birth. The calcium:phosphorous ratio is, as expected, ideal for skeletal growth, being on average 1.19:1.

Care of young

The female beaver is a very attentive mother. She stops whatever she is doing regularly to make special contact calls to her kits and to nuzzle them closely with her nose, keeping note of where they are all the time. When the young are confined to the nest, the mother returns every 30-40 minutes to check up on them by putting her head into the nest chamber and making the contact call, to which the young sometimes answer. Then she mostly enters the nest and, if they are asleep, she just checks them over with her nose, but if they are awake she continues to make the contact calls. Mother beavers also return rapidly to the nest if they hear the young making any noise. After contacting her young, the mother beaver inspects the territory and often digs as a form of displacement activity.

The kits leave the nest at between one and four days old, when they first bathe in the water basin in the lodge. They continue to do this until they are able to leave the lodge at night and spend some of their time in the open. Unable to dive until they are ten days old, kits cannot usually leave the lodge until then. Before swimming they must develop their escape behaviour and be able to groom themselves to ensure the water repellence of their fur. At 19 days old the mother stops supervising the indoor swimming sessions of her young. By this time the escape, grooming and swimming behaviours are all well developed and their ability to remain underwater is almost as good as adults'. By the time they leave the lodge for longer periods of time at one to two months old, beavers are able to look after themselves, but need the group for social contact. In fact once fully weaned at two months old, mothers are often aggressive to their kits if they become too demanding.

Moving young

Eurasian beaver mothers appear to be rather brutal when moving their young. They grasp them in their incisors either at the root of the tail or around their middles, especially when carrying them away for bathing. However, the kits do not seem to mind, remaining relaxed and still during this indignity. North American beavers seem more motherly: in Zurich Zoo they have been seen to carry their young in their arms and walk upright on their hind legs, in a smilar fashion to the way they transport food or building materials on land.

In order to encourage them to swim back to land after they first enter the water, mother beavers grasp their young in the same way, constantly changing their grip until the kits are pointing in a landward direction. Finally they are given a push with the nose on to dry land. At this stage, after bathing a couple of times, the young are carried or dragged back to the nest. Sometimes a young beaver is totally immersed in the water, being

Baby North American beaver being carried by its mother.

A young beaver's first outing from the lodge.

repeatedly carried back and forth, before being taken back to the nest for grooming. Mother beavers groom their young frequently and very intensely with their incisor teeth. They also clean the anal opening and eat any faeces produced by the young before they are allowed to bathe. After the first night's dip, young beavers are then able to get back out of the water without any assistance but even then the mother still retrieves them. By one week old the beaver kits have learnt the drill and return to the nest of their own accord if their mother attempts to grab them. Sometimes the mother dances aggressively towards the kits before trying to grab them; this also usually encourages them to return to the nest of their own accord.

Developing behaviours

Throughout this book I have described when beaver kits develop key behaviours. It seems that many of these behaviours are innate or easily stimulated, as even beavers reared artificially without parents soon develop survival skills for adult life.

Exploratory and threat behaviours

Beavers explore new surroundings just like other rodents. They are good at learning and remembering the layout of their home range. Young animals, who have found a new territory, patrol and inspect their territories regularly, thus reinforcing their knowledge of their surroundings. When beavers pair up, then both young adults share the task of inspecting their home range. Lactating females may also inspect the area, probably in order to ensure that their young are not threatened by any trespassers.

On the River Faxälv only subadult females have been seen to threaten beavers trespassing on their home range. Both sexes of adults probably defend the territory. Threat behaviours used to deter strange beavers include gnashing the teeth, tail movements and depositing castoreum. When the intruder finds that the castoreum matches the scent he has found on scent mounds, etc, in the territory, he should get the message and clear off.

If he fails to take the hint, he may be greeted by gnashing of teeth or slapping of tail. Teeth gnashing when threatening is similar to the movements used in tooth sharpening, but the lower jaw is thrust further forwards to allow for wider movements as the lower incisors grind against the upper ones. This sometimes makes a very loud and startling rattling sound. The tail is also important in threat displays, both visually and aurally. The tail is slapped down vertically on the ground, which is then followed by twitchings of the root of the tail and then by horizontal tail movements as the tail remains pressed against the ground.

Fighting

If a beaver is cornered by another, it does not immediately attack with its teeth, but instead makes a mock attack, either poking with its nose or just lightly snapping at its opponent's rear quarters. If beavers fight in water, they swim after each other in a very tight circle. These mock attacks are usually enough to deter a weaker opponent and this is always the case when a young beaver is being attacked by an adult.

However, if two adult beavers of about the same body size confront each other, the mock attacks can escalate to full-blown wrestling belly to belly. They wrestle on land or in shallow water by standing upright on

Wrestling.

their hind legs, using their tails for support and balance, and then swipe alternately with their forepaws, trying to grasp each other so that they can push their opponent backwards.

A beaver will fight more fiercely the nearer it is to its home lodge, and such fights may involve using the incisors as weapons. Bites may be directed over all the body, but those aimed at the hindquarters of the opponent may result in death, because the spinal cord at the root of the tail can be severed by a fierce bite. Although serious fights do occur occasionally, biting is usually strongly avoided, perhaps because it is so dangerous. In other words, beavers try hard to avoid being bitten and so get few opportunities to bite an opponent.

Social behaviour

Within a beaver group there is a strong social bond, even though individual beavers are independent when it comes to foraging, building dams and lodges etc. During active periods, beavers – particularly the adult pair – are always looking for opportunities to contact each other. Mutual grooming and over marking of scent mounds help to reinforce the social bonds within a group. However, if a group becomes so large that individuals begin to compete for food and other resources, beavers may become aggressive to each other; this is probably why beaver groups have never been recorded exceeding 18 animals.

Vocalisations

While outside the lodge beavers are strangely silent, emitting only a whistling call. This is a contact call directed to other group members who are out of sight. It is of very high frequency and may be difficult for people to hear, this presumably being an advantage in that potential predators may also not be able to hear and localise it. Perhaps the beaver's vulnerability to predators limits its desire to draw attention to itself with unnecessary calls. However, once indoors, beavers produce a variety of vocalisations. Seven different vocalisations have been heard from North American beavers (see box), and four of these have also been recorded from Eurasian beavers, although it is quite likely that they also have the same vocal repertoire.

When beavers are close together, there is less risk of them being heard, and they make a different vocalisation, which begins as a high-pitched squeak and develops into a longer series of both high and low-pitched sounds. Long series of these specially modulated contact calls are made by the adult pair or between group members when they are making deliberate social contact.

North American beaver vocalisations

1. Hiss: Beavers hiss when angry or scared.
2. Whine: A scarcely audible sound that is difficult to locate.
3. Cry: Often follows whining and sounds like a wailing child. Often made by a male when swimming towards a female that has called him or when fearing that food is about to be taken.
4. Nasal sound: Made when feeling good or in joyful anticipation e.g. when coming ashore for food. This sound is a vocal cord vibration made during inhalation.
5. Summons: A high-pitched straining call, repeated for a minute or more, often made by female to a male. A cry or summons call is usually made in response.
6. Soft churr: Made to a female or young siblings.
7. Guttural sound: A nondescript spluttering sound, which is made when a beaver is picked up.

Dancing in the water to stimulate mutual grooming.

Young beavers have been heard whimpering like small children if they are handled roughly. If young beavers of less than four weeks old are caught, they have been heard to make a clacking sound, but nobody knows what function this call has.

If a beaver is feeding and another group member approaches, it lets out a high-pitched whine which changes to a more aggressive sounding whine if the group member continues to approach. The message is clear: go away while I am feeding. Not all whining is negative though; when group members snuggle up to sleep in the lodge, they may produce a low whining noise just before they drop off to sleep.

While fighting beavers produce hoarse petulant sighs, but alarmed beavers produce a muted intermittent growling grunt.

Mutual grooming.

Contact and aggressive behaviour

Beavers display a variety of social behaviours, which involve contact. Some of these are clearly aggressive to varying degrees, while other are important for reinforcing the group's cohesion. Strange as it may seem from a human point of view, one of the more aggressive behaviours is dancing.

Dancing is similar to shaking water from the fur, but with more exaggerated head movements. It involves a beaver standing upright and making a series of body movements, which begin with the head being thrown backwards so that the nose moves in roughly a circular manner, and it continues with these movements as far back as the rear third of the body. Dancing appears to be a display by a dominant animal over another group member; an attempt to put another beaver firmly back in its place in the social hierarchy. Dancing seems to develop from sideways leaps performed by young beavers. Sometimes beavers snap at the fur of their opponents before dancing against a group member, who may well reciprocate before eventually fleeing.

Wrestling can also be a form of play, which may involve group members of all ages. A pair of beavers faces each other, usually while sitting in shallow water, and then begin to struggle with each other, often for many minutes. They push and grab at each other's neck and chest with their forepaws. They sometimes also swim with the upper body out of the water, trying to grab each other with mouth wide open. While this is all going on, they moan increasingly loudly and more frequently as the wrestling match intensifies.

At the other end of the social scale is mutual grooming, which decreases the aggressiveness or even shyness of other group members. Mutual grooming is a most important expression of social contact within the group, and is especially important in maintaining the pair bond between the adult pair, and in socialising young beavers within the group. It also serves another purpose: it allows beavers to get those parts of their bodies groomed that they cannot reach themselves and they readily take up a submissive posture to be groomed. This helps maintain the water repellence and heat insulating properties of their fur, so that beavers in a group are dependent on each other for this important social and maintenance function. Young beavers begin to mutually groom other beavers at the end of the maternal period, just when aggression is building between mother and young. In unpaired beavers, mutual grooming often begins after dancing, once dominance has been established or reinforced.

Forming pairs

Beavers may form pairs with members of the opposite sex as yearlings in their first autumn, although it is more usual for dispersal and pair formation to occur in the second year. At first they isolate themselves in their own tunnel system, presumably to get to know each other better, because at first they spend all their time here together. In one case on the River Faxälv, a new pair had extended their tunnel system to over 100 metres in length by the following May when the female was pregnant. During pair formation, the two beavers continually look for each other for mutual grooming or they make frequent contact calls. It has been suggested that pairs usually form where the female is dominant to the male, and involves the female depositing castoreum in the new home range before pair formation, although these observations were made on captive animals and may not be representative of the wild. In captivity the pair may remain aggressive to each other for the first two weeks or so after first meeting, before eventually calming down and grooming each other. In due course an equal partnership showing no dominance develops.

Parasites

The beaver beetle *(Platypsyllus castoris)*, is only about 3 mm long and looks at first glance rather like a cross between a flea and a woodlouse. Its flattened shape is clearly an adaptation to remaining firmly fixed to a beaver whether it is in the water or on land. Of more than 350,000 species of beetle that are known worldwide, the beaver beetle is one of only two that has opted for a parasitic lifestyle.

Beaver beetles are found on both species of beavers, but there is another species, *Leptinillus validus*, which is found only on North American beavers. It is not true to describe beaver beetles as wholly parasitic, even though they apparently occasionally feed on the blood and fatty tissue of the host, which could be regarded as damaging. In some ways they can be regarded as commensals or even beneficial, as they eat up dead skin cells (i.e. dandruff) and hair and they feed on mites *(Schizocarpus mingaundi)*, thus helping to

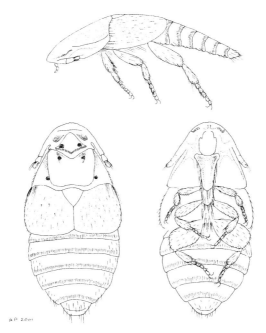

Beaver beetle.

control numbers of a parasite that feeds on beaver hairs.

Beaver beetles have an unusual lifestyle for a beetle. The eggs and pupae are laid in the nesting material within the beavers' lodges, and the newly-hatched larvae then have every opportunity of climbing onto a beaver, when they develop into adults.

Other ectoparasitical fur-eaters include the mites *Trichodectes castoris* and *Haemogamsus* sp. The tick *Ixodes banksi* is commonly found on North American beavers (e.g. 55% in one sample); some individuals have to put up with up to 106 ticks! Leeches have also been found taking advantage of ulcerated sores on North American beavers.

Endoparasites of beavers include liver flukes (*Fasciola* sp.), a trematode (*Stichorepis subtriquetrus*) and the nematode worms *Ascaris castoroides* (in North American beavers only), *Castrostrongylus castoris* and *Travossius rufus*. Although endoparasites are often found in beavers, they are not thought to control populations.

One bacterial disease, tularaemia, affects the liver, spleen, lungs and lymph nodes of North American beavers, particularly in the north-east, resulting in die-offs, which have made a major impact on the hunting of beavers in the past. For example in Saskatchewan in 1800 the beaver succumbed to a 'distemper' (probably tularaemia). Fortunately, Eurasian beavers are resistant to this disease.

Mortality

Eurasian beavers live for about 7-8 years on average. The oldest wild beaver lived on the Lipetsk Forestry Station in Voronezh, Russia, from 1910 to 1932 and was estimated to be 25 years old when it died. Very few beavers live to this great age though. In a sample of 15,000 North American beavers, only one reached the age of 20. Even so, compared with many other mammals (e.g. otters, foxes and wildcats), beavers are relatively long-lived mammals.

However, mortality acts on the beaver population in different ways in different areas from before implantation of embryos in the womb to old age. For example, in North American beavers 3.8-38.2% of embryos are lost before implantation, with another 2.7-17.2% lost before birth, although foetuses are not known to be lost once hair has begun to develop. The causes of this pre-birth mortality are unknown.

Mortality remains fairly low until after the first year when young beavers begin the process of becoming independent. Some places are worse than others: on the River Elbe in Germany annual adult deaths were running at 46.6% over three and a half years with a further 25.5% being injured by other beavers. This problem occurred mostly in spring, when fighting broke out between adults during the breeding season.

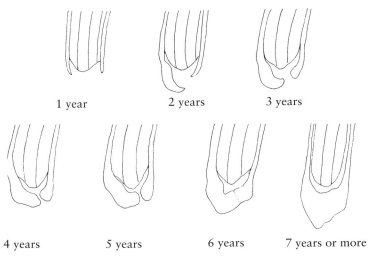

1 year   2 years   3 years

4 years   5 years   6 years   7 years or more

Ageing beavers from X-rays of their cheek teeth.

Most adults die from severe winter weather, starvation and malnutrition while under the ice during the winter; fluctuating water levels, especially floods, which result in drowning; falling trees and hunting by predators and humans also cause mortality. The main factor affecting natural population growth of beavers is the availability of food in the winter. As population densities increase in a particular area, mortality rates increase, birth rates and litter sizes decline, and sexual maturity and dispersal from the natal lodge are delayed.

Ageing beavers

Beavers can be aged in various ways: by using the relationship between skull length and body weight; sectioning teeth and looking at the annual layers of dentine and cementum in the molars and tooth root closure. However, the one disadvantage of all these is that the beaver has to be dead to carry them out. Recently, Dr Göran Hartman of the Swedish University of Agricultural Sciences in Uppsala has developed a method for ageing live beavers based on radiographs of beaver jaws. With increasing age, the open roots of beaver molars close up and become filled in with an increasingly thick layer of cementum. From the degree of closure and in-filling, it is possible to determine the age of a living beaver up to about seven years of age, when the teeth are fully developed.

History in Europe

Beavers were once found throughout much of Europe, excluding only Ireland, much of southern Italy and the southern Balkans and Greece, where they never apparently colonised. By the end of sixteenth century beavers had disappeared from Britain, and much of Denmark and Belgium. By this time beaver skins had reached very high prices; in 1591 in eastern Prussia, beaver skins had reached the same value as bear skins (1.5 Marks each). Beaver hunting became a feudal right, the violation of which was punishable by the death penalty. Being aquatic, beavers were classed as fish and could be eaten on a Friday. No doubt this added to the demand for the beaver both by monks and the wider population.

A century later the situation had worsened considerably with beavers now absent from the Iberian Peninsula, western France and all of Italy. Beavers had also all but disappeared from Finland. During the eighteenth century beavers now also become very scarce in much of northern Russia and extinct in France (except in the Rhone). At the beginning of the nineteenth century the beaver's distribution was severely fragmented with only isolated populations in Russia, the Baltic states, southern, central and northern Scandinavia, the Caucasus, Turkey, and central and eastern Europe. The situation continued to worsen, almost to the point of extinction so that at the beginning of the twentieth century only a few hundred at most European beavers survived in the Rhone in France, the Elbe in Germany, southern Norway and a few scattered and isolated populations in Russia. The cause of this decline was mostly hunting for fur, meat and castoreum, but habitat loss probably also played its part, particularly during the nineteenth century when many wetlands were drained in order to improve agriculture.

However, during the nineteenth century there was growing awareness of the plight of the beaver and many countries introduced legislation to protect them, even if in several cases this only occurred after its extinction e.g. in Sweden, where legal protection came in 1873, two years after the species' demise. Moreover, during the twentieth century there were effective conservation measures such as reintroductions, which have seen the beaver spread far and wide throughout Europe especially in the latter half of the twentieth century.

Fossil beavers in Britain

The earliest British beavers were the Eurasian beaver, *Castor fiber*, and the small *Trogontherium minus*, the ancestor of the Eurasian giant beaver, which were both found about two million years ago in what we call today Suffolk. *T. minus* gave rise to *T. cuvieri,* which increased in size until it reached a maximum in the Cromerian 700,000 years ago, and then it declined in size before becoming extinct in the Hoxnian/Holsteinian, about 375,000 years ago. It has been suggested that by declining in size, this brought it into competition with the Eurasian beaver, resulting in its eventual demise. However, this cannot be a convincing explanation because the two species must have filled distinct ecological niches in order for selection pressures to be able to cause the decline in size of *Trogontherium*. In fact it is likely that *Trogontherium* occupied the lower reaches of rivers and floodplains, and effectively excluded the Eurasian beaver from these habitats. In contrast the Eurasian beaver showed no obvious pattern of size change and survived until after the last Ice Age, when hunting by humans caused its disappearance. Not only are beaver bones found as fossils, but the wood they have gnawed may also be preserved. Identified by the distinctive tooth marks at the ends, these pieces of wood can also be dated by various methods so that we know beavers have been gnawing away in Britain for at least 700,000 years.

Beaver fossils and archaeological remains have been found at 104 different sites in Britain dating from the Pliocene to the Medieval period. Most date from the middle Holocene or Neolithic archaeological period from about 5,800 to 4,500 years ago and they are distributed primarily in southern central England, East Anglia, Yorkshire and the eastern Borders of Scotland. However, this distribution has little ecological meaning as it reflects mostly suitable deposits in which remains have been preserved rather than necessarily being evidence for optimal habitats in the past.

Evidence for the existence of beavers in Britain in the more recent past not only comes from fossils and fossil wood, but also historical records. Derek Yalden of Manchester University has been researching the mainly Old Norse and Old English place names in Britain that are based on the names of extinct mammals such as the wolf, bear, wild pig and beaver. Only nineteen place names could be found that commemorate the beaver and some of these might have been confused with the verb 'to beaver', which referred to the fermentation of woad in a 'beaver pit'. However, by looking at the context of the place, it was possible to determine with a fair degree of certainty whether a particular place name does refer to a rodent. For example, Beverley in Yorkshire is close to the Humber marshes, and Beverley Brook on the River Thames at Battersea was associated with the Thames marshes and these locations would be more likely to be homes to beavers rather than beaver pits. No beaver place names could be found in Scotland even though we know beavers lived there from fossil evidence; Beverkae in Fife was found to be a 19th century invention with no historical basis in real beavers.

The documentary evidence for the British beaver is also rather sparse. The earliest mention is in the *The Laws of Hywel Dda*, which is said to date from A.D. 940 and which gives the prices of furs, including the beaver. At that time the beaver's pelt was worth 120 pence, which was considerably greater than the prices for an otter pelt (12 pence) or a pine marten pelt (24 pence). Indeed this high price has been used as evidence to suggest that beavers were already becoming rare.

For our next reference to the beaver, we must turn to Scotland, where the beaver is mentioned among other furbearers in the export duties for furs during the reign of King David I (1124-1153). This document is known as the *Assisa Regis David de Tolloneis*. The next historical reference to the beaver is that of Giraldus Cambrensis or Gerald de Barri who toured Wales in 1188 with the Archbishop of Canterbury. This account is the only description of the natural history of the beaver in Britain and confirmed that the beaver was becoming very rare indeed: 'The Teivi has another singular particularity, being the only river in Wales, or even in England, which has beavers; in Scotland they are said to be found in one river but are very scarce.' Gerald de Barri described many aspects of the beaver's natural history accurately either from first hand observation or by talking with hunters, but he still quotes the old castration stories from bestiaries (see p.25).

The beaver is also mentioned in the *Ayr Manuscript*, which was probably written at a parliament in Ayr during the reign of Robert the Bruce (1306-1329). It is mentioned in a chapter entitled 'peloure or peltry', which lists the commoner animal skins of the time, on which export duty was to be paid. Curiously, it also mentions the sable *Martes zibellina*, which has never been native to Britain, which has led some observers to suggest that beaver skins may have been imported for re-export. The *beveris*, as it was called, was omitted from a similar list in an Act of

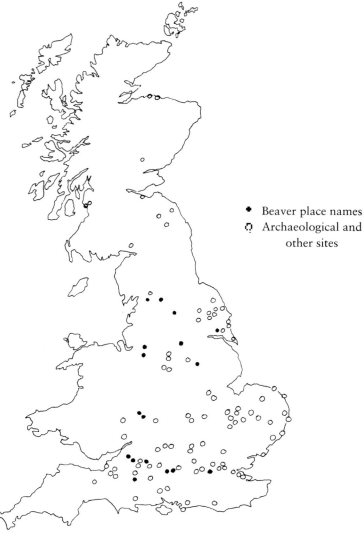

A map of Britain showing beaver place names, literature records, and fossil and archaeological sites.

Parliament of James I (1406-1437), dating from June 1424, suggesting either extinction or at least commercial extinction. In other words, perhaps there were just not enough beavers to hunt any more? The beaver was also missing from a list of fur-bearing mammals on which export duty was to be paid in 1482, when shipped through the port of Leith on the Firth of Forth.

The last historical mention of British beavers was that of Boethius or Hector Boece who in 1526 mentioned in his *Cronikils of Scotland* that along with other game animals, the beaver was still very abundant in and around Loch Ness and this was apparently still the case ten years later when his book was translated into English by Bellenden.

The only other recent reference to the beaver dates back to the early nineteenth century, when Patrick Neil claimed that some Gaelic speakers in Argyll still spoke of the *losleathan* (broad-tail) or *dobhran losleathan* (broad-tailed otter), which refer clearly to the beaver (even though it was long extinct) and which are very similar to the Welsh name for the beaver (*llost lydan)* in *The Laws of Hywel Dda*. Another Welsh name, *afanc,* is now thought to refer to a mythical monster or the otter rather than the beaver as was once believed.

Recent history in Britain: New World interlopers

In the nineteenth century there was enormous enthusiasm for introducing and exploiting exotic animals in Europe. This was led by acclimatisation societies, which were established in most European countries during the nineteenth century. With the Eurasian beaver continuing to decline and become extinct in many countries in Europe, it is perhaps not too surprising that the landed gentry began to dabble with North American beavers. The British Acclimatisation Society was founded in 1860 and beavers were identified as one of many species that were expected to become successfully acclimatised to Britain.

During the nineteenth century there were four well-known attempts to establish North American beavers in Britain. None were introductions as the beavers were released in to enclosures, but in some cases there were escapes and for some time at least these escapees bred successfully, although none of the populations became established. The first attempt was in 1870 when a number of beavers escaped from their enclosure in Sotterley Park, near Beccles in Suffolk. They were free for two years and bred so successfully that they travelled some 6-8 km to colonise Benacre Broad, but all had been either exterminated or had died out by 1872.

After an apparently unsuccessful attempt a year earlier, in 1875 the Marquess of Bute released seven beavers into an enclosure of about 4 acres near Kilchattan Bay on the Isle of Bute. Although the surviving beavers were North American, we know that Scandinavian beavers were released into the enclosure, but these do not seem to have survived. The North American beavers did well at first and increased to 16 animals by 1878 and even more by 1879. Their history has been well documented and the colony seemed to be thriving. However, the last beaver from this enclosure was recorded in about 1887, but remains of the dams could still be seen in 1918.

Coincidentally, just as the last of the Bute beavers died, so Sir Edmund Loder released some North American beavers into an enclosure on his estate at Leonardslee near Horsham in Sussex. This group survived until 1938 with the addition of only two more animals in 1917. The ninth Duke of Argyll introduced two male and five female North American beavers into the grounds of Inverary castle in Argyllshire in 1902 after a month of acclimatisation in a holding pen. Another two males and three females were introduced the following year, but no more was heard of these beavers except for a single dead animal recorded in the same year.

There have also been occasional escapes of North American beavers. For example, single beavers have been recorded from Essex and Somerset; the latter individual survived in the wild for at least eight years. Finally, just as Scottish Natural Heritage began to explore the feasibility of reintroducing the Eurasian beaver to Britain in 1995, four young North American beavers escaped from a private collection based on the south-eastern shore of Loch Lomond at Cameron House. Overcrowding in their enclosure coupled with poor fencing led to a dramatic dispersal. Two animals were found alive in Renfrewshire, having swum down the River Leven and across the Clyde, but sadly the individual that travelled the greatest distance (24 miles as the crow flies), was run over by a car at Glen Falloch, near Crianlarich in Perthshire. Its skin and skeleton are preserved in the National Museums of Scotland in Edinburgh.

Castoreum as a commodity

The use of castoreum as a medicine has been known since ancient times. For example, in 500 B.C. Hippocrates (he of the oath) wrote of the medicinal properties of castoreum in the treatment of diseases of the womb, and in 7 B.C. Strabo claimed that Spanish castoreum was not as good as the Italian product. Therefore, castoreum has until recently always been regarded as a valuable medicinal commodity but it also had other uses. In the Middle Ages it was used by bee-keepers to deter wasps and other hymenopteran predators from hives, thereby increasing honey production. In 1734 the father of scientific nomenclature, Carl Linné, better known as Linnaeus, recommended the Lapps' practice of mixing their snuff with castoreum. However, most castoreum was used for its medicinal properties. Some proposed that it was a panacea that could be used to treat all ills and ailments, but others were more specific and reserved it for the treatment of ear ache, constipation, sores, ulcers, dysmenorrhoea, arthritic pains and it could also be used as a sedative and a tonic by dissolving it in alcohol. Beaver skins were also apparently used to treat gout, arthritis and rheumatism, presumably through external application. The German naturalist Peter Pallas reported that beavers from the Terek, Sunzha, Alazan and Kura Rivers of Russia produced castoreum of high value; about 50% of the castoreum from these beavers was soluble in alcohol compared with only 12% for Canadian beavers. Not surprisingly, castoreum has reached very high prices in the past, but eventually prices crashed as modern medicines were developed. For example, in 1852 a castor sac from a German beaver was worth 720 Marks, whereas by 1924 in London one pound of castoreum was worth only 4-5 dollars.

There has been much debate about how efficacious castoreum actually is. Castoreum may contain a chemical similar to acetylsalicylic acid (the active ingredient of aspirin, see p. 76), which the beaver concentrates from the bark of willow trees or from meadowsweet. Presumably in those areas where willows or meadowsweet are either absent or comprise only a small proportion of the diet, little or no aspirin-like active ingredient will be present in the castoreum. Perhaps this has led to the variation in observed effectiveness of castoreum as a medicine as recorded by different practitioners.

Beaver fur and hats

The use of beaver fur in Britain is known as far back as Saxon times as shown by the discovery of some beaver fur, which may have formed a bag to protect a lyre, in the Sutton Hoo ship burial in Suffolk. Beaver fur was undoubtedly used widely throughout Europe and North America for hats and clothing for thousands of years. Beaver fur was probably originally used for hats in the Middle Ages because beavers were considered intelligent animals, owing to their construction skills, so that a hat made from its fur would be expected to be of benefit to the wearer, even if it only stopped head aches.

Furs were not normal everyday wear in Britain during the second half of the seventeenth century, except on formal occasions, and beaver felt hats were the ultimate expression of style and fashion. Beaver felt is a very light, strong and waterproof material and hence was ideal for hat making, especially for the often damp British weather. The dense smooth short hairs (10 mm long) with their fine crimp (of some 8-10 μm) gives beaver underfur its ability to make good quality felt. However, to use the felt for hat making, the outer coarse guard hairs had to be removed first. In the mid-seventeenth century this was done by first sending the furs to Russia, where they were worn as the linings to cloaks. After much wear the guard hairs would fall out leaving the old, dirty, greasy underfur, which was ideal for felting. Therefore, beaver skins could be sold for double profit: first as clothing and then for felting. Perhaps this is one of the earliest examples of a recycling industry? North American beaver skins worn by Indians were also much sought after for felting, because the guards hairs had been lost and they were suitably greasy and sweaty for this process.

One of the earliest historical references in Britain to beaver hats was by Geoffrey Chaucer in the late 14th century who confessed to wearing a 'Flaundryssh bever hat'. Hats were initially imported to Britain until religious refugees from Rheims in France, who just happened to include felt makers, settled in Southwark in London in 1517. The most popular style of hats worn in the early 16th century were similar in appearance to the caps of the Yeoman of the Guard at the Tower of London. There were also variations on this basic style of hat including the Milan bonnet, which had a very deep upturned brim. The brim was also often split into sections so that, rather like a deerstalker, it was possible to pull these down to cover the nape, ears and eyes, or hold them up with laces in various combinations. By the second half of the sixteenth century the height of the crown of the hat became more important than the brim and beaver hats were reaching very high prices. Beaver hats were still imported from Europe and reached prices of 20 shillings or more; in 1586 a notable Puritan, Philip Stubbes, complained that 40 shillings was an outrageous price to pay for this necessary fashion item, which could be bought in a myriad of shapes, styles and decorations. However, most working people had flat caps, which were often made of felt or were knitted and then felted. It was not until the 17th century that felt hats replaced fabric hats as everyday wear. Less than a century later in 1661 Samuel Pepys noted that a hat cost him the considerable sum of 45 shillings. By this time the

1346

1386

1470

1435

1485

1578

1606

1628

1640

1745

1757

1785

1810

Beaver hats from the 14th to the 19th centuries.

production of beaver hats had begun in Britain, although most of the fur probably came from North America as most European populations were probably too small to be commercially exploited, except in some areas of Scandinavia, the Baltic and Russia. Beaver hats continued to be used until the 1840s, when the latest fashion in high hats required a high gloss effect using silk. The new technology that was developed to satiate this demand meant the end of the beaver hat and it has been suggested that it probably saved the beaver from extinction both in Europe and North America.

Exploitation in the New World

By the late 16th century beavers were largely extinct in western Europe, and only small supplies could be obtained from Russia and Scandinavia. The Scandinavian trade was controlled through the Baltic ports by the Hanseatic League. This monopoly was broken in 1555 when the Muscovy Company was established in Britain to open up new exports from Russia. However, continuing trading problems with the Russian czars meant that new sources of beavers were sought elsewhere.

From the mid 16th century beaver pelts from North America began to find their way to Europe as a by-product of the cod-fishing industry. These pelts were traded on a small scale from North American Indians on the eastern seaboard. Before Europeans began trading in North American beaver furs, beavers were hunted by North American Indians for both food and fur. In addition their incisor teeth were turned into gouges, chisels and knives. The fatty tails were a particular delicacy and fur robes were highly prized and are known from fragments up to 2,500 years old. Beaver meat was probably particularly sought after because compared with deer meat it is three times more digestible as it contains more fat. It is not surprising, therefore, that beaver bones are often the most abundant of all animal remains in middens (rubbish dumps) at Indian archaeological sites. Beavers were also probably easier to hunt than deer and were captured by a variety of methods including: clubs, arrows, lances, nets and deadfall traps; tactics involved waiting in ambush behind willow-baited blinds, and at ice holes in the winter after scaring the beavers from their lodges, and breaking their dams or making calls to attract the beavers.

Although the North American Indians treated beavers with great respect because of their highly developed social life, the attraction of European goods resulted in an ever-increasing trade in their pelts.

The apparently huge trade in beaver skins – about 100,000 pelts annually – had a great effect on local Indians; their way of life changed from subsistence hunting for food and other resources to commercial hunting for beaver pelts. In this way local Indians became increasingly dependent on European goods in order to survive. The Europeans needed to export huge volumes of pelts in order to finance the transportation costs to Europe. This resulted in local over-exploitation and extinction, and, as prices for pelts rose locally, so the middlemen tried to control the trade even more, but the Europeans generally overcame these problems and the resulting high prices by moving further westwards and southwards in search of new areas and populations to exploit.

If it were not for beaver skins, and the sixteenth-century demand for beaver hats, the country now known as Canada might not exist today, and if it did, it would never have been explored and colonised so quickly by Europeans. The British, in particular, seemed to search unendingly for the North West Passage to the Pacific Ocean, which led in part to a trade in beaver skins with the local Indian populations. This was so successful that the Hudson Bay Company was established in 1670 and given exclusive rights to beaver furs throughout Prince Rupert Land, which extended over much of central Canada, centred on Hudson's Bay.

So huge was the trade in beaver furs that it could support itself and the trade in other furs, despite continuing high transportation costs. Land-based trade in beaver pelts expanded rapidly and continued for the next 250 years until there was literally nowhere else to go in North America.

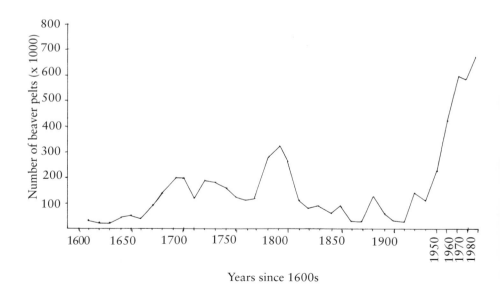

Graph to show beaver pelt numbers taken in North America since 1600s to present day

From the beaver's perspective the impact was that local over-exploitation led to a shift in the trade to elsewhere.

The most significant event, as far as beavers were concerned, was the merger of the famous Hudson Bay Company with the North West Company in 1821. By this time beavers were becoming very scarce in the region to the south and east of the Churchill River. Aware of this, the Hudson Bay Company had a virtual monopoly in the beaver fur trade in Canada and tried to implement conservation measures to protect beaver populations and allow their sustainable exploitation. Each region was divided into trading districts, for which there was a rigid quota of pelts based on beaver numbers. There were closed and open trapping seasons, and summer and cub beaver were not trapped for the trade. By 1840 this was beginning to bring some success, but at that time the market collapsed. The silk hat came into vogue and the demand for beaver fur for hats disappeared. By 1900 the beaver was either very scarce or extinct over much of the USA. Mink and raccoon furs displaced the beaver as the main fur producer. However, in Canada, the boreal forests are unsuitable for farming, and the cutting down of the forests on the Canadian Shield during the nineteenth century created valuable wetland habitat dominated by the beaver's favourite food, aspen, which led to a recovery in beaver numbers. Conservation measures in North America during the twentieth century also led to an increase in the numbers and distribution of beavers, so that trapping of beavers for their fur has continued until the present day.

Despite the collapse in the use of beaver fur for felting during the 1830s and 1840s, the trade in beaver pelts increased steadily again during the nineteenth century until in 1876 when they were once more the predominant fur on the market. However, the numbers of beaver pelts began to decline at this period in time, as trappers could no longer expand their operations into new areas. North America was all used up! The recovery of the trade in beaver furs was caused by a massive ten-fold increase in the export of furs to Britain from 1860 to 1880 with a 40% price increase, and the USA became a net importer of furs by three-fold during the late nineteenth century.

We often think of the early trade in beaver pelts as being so huge that this led to the North American beaver's imminent extinction. However, the numbers of pelts that were traded do not support this view, even though local extinctions were common. Peak trade produced 401,000 pelts in 1793, but only an average of between 100,000 to 300,000 annually during much of the eighteenth and nineteenth centuries. In contrast, in the 1970s and 1980s between 450,000 and one million beavers were trapped for their fur each year in North America. However, whatever the numbers, beaver fur was the most highly valued fur prior to the twentieth century, and today populations in North America and Europe are probably more stable and secure than they have been for 500 years.

Reintroductions

The reintroduction of the beaver in Europe has been an outstanding success, even though very few of these attempts are likely to have followed IUCN reintroduction guidelines.

Reintroduced populations show a high rate of increase (20-34% per year), but this slows down as populations become established and optimal habitat gets used up, so that beaver groups are forced to compete with each other. In Poland almost half a century after reintroduction, population growth rates were far more modest (0-15%); similar low rates of increase were recorded on the Elbe (7% annually, 1948-1971) and in Norway (5-6% per annum, 1880-1965). This decline in population growth appears to occur at group densities of about 0.2-0.25 per km². However, in most countries in Europe colony density is well below this (e.g. 0.06-0.2 colonies per km² in Sweden and 0.15 km² in the Suwalki Lakeland of Poland).

Beavers need about 3 km of river bank for a territory (i.e. 1.5 km of river length), although, depending on food quality, season and social factors, territories may vary from 0.5 to 12.8 km of river. In general territories increase in the spring and summer as beavers try to find enough food to live on, but they shrink back to a length that is easily patrolled in winter without the beavers losing condition e.g. 7.9 km in the Netherlands.

Although most beaver impacts on the environment are positive or benign as far as human activities are concerned, there may be some direct economic impacts, which farmers and other land users may find difficult to live with. Flooding may affect roads, fields, sewerage and other waste systems and may damage timber and fruit trees. They may also block or damage dykes, dams, culverts and drains and inadvertently destroy valuable habitats and rare species.

Management

Undoubtedly following a reintroduction, some people are not going to enjoy the experience of having beavers on their land. However, we should not necessarily be too concerned about this, because our colleagues in Europe and North America have been living alongside beavers for hundreds and thousands of years, so that there are a whole range of methods of overcoming any problems that may arise. We can build on their experience and technology to suit our own needs.

For example, valuable trees can be protected in a variety of ways, including the use of wire mesh or sheets of galvanised metal to protect the trunk from very sharp incisors. Electric fencing and even commercially available deer repellents such as Thiram, Magic Circle and TNB-A (10% trinitrobenzene-aniline) may apparently deter beavers for up to three years after application. Artificial scent mounds may also be used to drive away beavers, especially with the application of some strange castoreum and when placed near to the inhabited lodge, and Frank Rosell's experiments with carnivore odours show that these have potential for deterring beavers too (see p.81). If that does not work, artificial feeding may divert their attention, although you will probably end up with more beavers. If there is no alternative, there are tried and tested methods for shooting and trapping beavers, which are used to effectively control local populations. As a by-product beavers are still harvested for their fur, and their meat can be cooked in variety of ways. However, recently Frank Rosell has developed a successful method for live trapping beavers using a net from a boat, so that they can be moved away from conflict areas.

Where beaver dams have raised water levels too high and the beavers refuse to be deterred, a pipe can be inserted through the dam or blocked culvert to allow water to flow through, thereby reducing water levels. The beavers do not respond to hidden leaks, and so can continue to live happily alongside their humans neighbours.

Recolonising a landscape

Reintroductions have given us unique opportunities to look at what beavers think are optimal habitats without the problem of having to compete with their fellow beavers. They also allow us to examine the pattern in which beavers recolonise landscapes and indeed even how to predict this. Beavers are described as choosy generalists when it comes to both food and habitat. When moving into new areas they choose the most desirable residences and only when market demand outstrips supply do they end up in secondary locations, as estate agents would describe them.

In the Grimsö Wildife Research Area (GWRA) in south central Sweden, two beaver groups were first recorded in 1980. By 1992 ten groups occupied the same area, but the river is too wide for the beavers to construct dams. GWRA is in the southern boreal zone and comprises coniferous forest and bogs with about 15% deciduous trees along the river banks, including birch, black alder, willows and aspen. Each beaver group occupies about one kilometre of water course or two kilometres of banks. By analysing the physical and biological components of habitats, it was hoped to discover what makes a beaver family recognise a particular piece of river as an ideal home.

It was found that the presence of summer food items (grasses and herbaceous plants) and high levels of tortuosity (degree of meandering of the river) were the two most important things a beaver wants in a territory. Clearly a good summer food source is important in areas where the lack of any felled trees by beavers does not allow a vigorous understorey to develop. Meandering rivers have a slower flow, which means that lodges, dams and winter stores are less likely to be swept away in the spate. Other factors, which were less important, included the width and depth of the river, and the consistency of the soil. Very wide rivers are probably avoided because they are not deep enough and may be covered by ice for a greater proportion of the year. Deeper water was preferred to allow for diving, cacheing winter food supplies and hiding burrow entrances. And soft soil is preferred because it is easier to dig (and may be better for the beavers' favourite trees). Even less significant were the slope of the bank

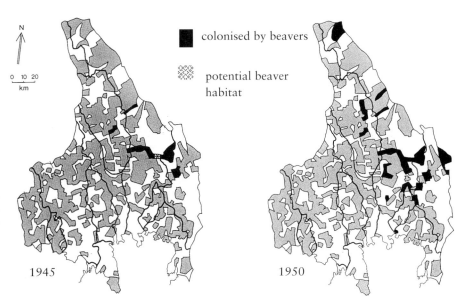

Colonisation by beavers at Värmland in Sweden, 1945-87 (Hartman, 1995).

1960

1970

1980

1987

of the river (very steep ones avoided) and the degree of shrub cover. Although there tended to be more deciduous forest in occupied areas, the proportion in the riparian zone (beside the river bank) was not important, suggesting that all sites had tree cover above a certain minimum threshold.

In summary beavers prefer mature river valleys with meandering water courses, but their activities help create some of these effects, so giving a river the appearance of having a much greater age.

Dr Göran Hartman has mapped the pattern of spread of reintroduced beavers in Värmland, southern Sweden, based on sightings by moose (*Alces alces*) hunters. The beavers were first reintroduced to this region in 1925 and only twenty years later they had spread rapidly 122 km north-west, but only 38 km to the south-east. By 1950 the spread to the north-west had reached 306 km from the reintroduction point. However, in general the dispersal was quite limited, mostly to the same drainage basin, and colonisation was very patchy. By 1960 it was clear that people were becoming impatient for the beavers to cross into a different drainage system in the west and so ten beavers were translocated there and subsequent recolonisation was very rapid. Full recolonisation had been achieved by 1987, some half a century after the initial reintroduction. This kind of recolonisation pattern has also been observed in Poland and Germany. It is thought that beavers do not just set up home a few kilometres along the same river, but search out either optimum habitats or mates. Of course, by spreading so widely at first, there is a real danger that the recolonisation process is slowed down as beavers find themselves in areas with no other beavers at all. Once the optimal sites have been used up and population densities begin to rise, so the beavers are then forced to colonise less suitable habitat and fill in the gaps between.

Genetic variability in reintroduced beavers in Sweden

One of the major concerns about any reintroduction is that if too few individuals are used, high levels of inbreeding could result. Inbreeding is generally damaging to animal populations, because rare deleterious genes may by chance become fixed by genetic drift in small populations, thereby resulting eventually in their demise. This situation may be exacerbated where the source population has undergone its own population bottleneck in the past, so that much genetic variation may already have been lost. The concern is that there may not be enough genetic variation in these populations for them to survive the environmental changes of the future, even if they seem successful today.

Given that taxonomic studies suggest Scandinavian beavers should be reintroduced to Britain, this concern could be very valid. Beavers became extinct in Sweden in the 1870s and the Norwegian population probably declined to about 100 individuals by 1888. From 1922 to 1946 a total of 46 beavers were reintroduced successfully at eleven sites in Sweden. Today there is an astonishing population of more than 100,000 animals all derived from these 46 founders.

To see if the population bottlenecks caused by the original population decline and subsequent reintroduction had damaged genetic variation in Swedish beavers, variation in the major histocompatibility complex (MHC) was studied using genetic fingerprinting. The MHC controls our ability to produce antibodies to fight diseases and a high genetic variation may be regarded as desirable in populations to allow them to respond to changing conditions in the future. The results confirmed suspicions that genetic variability was low in Swedish beavers (equivalent to highly inbred burrowing rodent groups or island carnivores), but it was equally low in Norwegian beavers, who have not been reintroduced, showing that reintroductions had not caused this low figure compared with Russian beavers from bigger more diverse populations. Whereas there was no variation in Swedish beavers and significant variation in Russian beavers in terms of MHC, there was little genetic difference between the two. This is probably because the populations of reintroduced beavers grew so rapidly in the optimal habitat that was available.

Fortunately, Scandinavian beavers seem to be very tolerant of inbreeding, so that we should not expect any deterioration in the genetic variability of beavers reintroduced from there to Scotland. However, a question mark still hangs over whether future environmental changes may adversely affect reintroduced beaver populations. Perhaps a more detailed taxonomic study will confirm that Russian and Scandinavian beavers are close enough that Russian beavers could be used to reinforce the genetically poor population of Sweden and hopefully Scotland.

A beaver recipe

When beavers become very abundant, it will become our duty to try and help limit numbers given that there are hardly any natural predators in Britain. What better sign of success of a reintroduction project than if we can all enjoy eating beaver meat. Several recipes by Reidun Moseid of Farsund and Peik Bendixen of Trondheim were published by the Environmental Protection Department of Vest-Agder province, Norway, in a series of three leaflets. I am most grateful to Duncan Halley for kindly translating them for our benefit.

To make the taste of the meat milder and to remove the blood, immerse the meat in a blend of 10 l. water, 200 g salt, and 20-30 ml. vinegar. Knead the meat occasionally. After two days rinse thoroughly in clean water and drain. The meat is now ready for cooking or for freezing. Alternatively, a good result can also be obtained by immersing the beaver meat in milk for 24 hours before cooking.

Beaver meat can be combined in cooking with other game, and there are countless possibilities for further preparation: casseroles; steak; meatcakes; etc.

Here is an example of a traditional beaver recipe:

Beaver tail soup

Use the meaty part of the beaver tail from the base forward to the beginning of the scaly part of the tail (about one third of the way from base to tip). The thickest part of the scaly portion of the tail can also be used once the scales are cleaned off. Do not remove the fat. For this recipe, the meat does not require preparatory soaking in water, salt and vinegar as described above. Divide the tail crosswise in smaller pieces, 3-4 cm long.

1.5– 2 litres water
salt
pepper
a little thyme and sage and a lovage leaf
150g celery
a medium large leek
2 large carrots
finely chopped parsley
2 cloves
2 bay leaves

Boil the meat with the salt, pepper and seasonings until it is quite tender. Add the vegetables and boil further until they are tender. The fat, which has not melted, has a jelly-like consistency and a very piquant taste.

Bringing beavers back to Britain

The Eurasian beaver has been absent from Britain for at least 450 years and many people now feel that it is time that Europe's largest rodent is restored to Britain's countryside. This idea was first floated seriously in the 1970s, but this notion was soundly put down by Sir Christopher Lever, who has documented the consequences of introducing non-native species all around the world. Despite the beaver once being indigenous, Lever believed that Britain no longer had suitable habitat for this species and any reintroduction would be bound to lead to conflict with people.

Good reasons to do it

On the other hand, the beaver is believed to bring many benefits to Britain's ecology: their dams sustain water flow and help prevent flooding during spate. There is also a gradual release of water during dry periods, and seasonal variations are reduced. Most of the energy dissipated by the stream is at the dams, where plunge pools develop below the dams. (Though large beaver ponds may result in high evaporation and reduced water flow.) The diversity of aquatic habitats of the riparian zone increases in complexity with varying water table levels, soil-water regimes and stream flow paths. A complex network of channels develops particularly in low elevations. Stability of the river and stream channels is better.

More sediments are stored in streams behind dams so that less sediment is lost by the river catchment. The sediments of the stream become sorted according to size with coarser sediments just below the dams and finer above them. Organic matter entering the water course is stored, processed and decomposes more locally to where it is produced than if it were swept down without the dams.

There is a several hundred-fold increase in the wetted surface area of the water course, which leads to an increase in pH from 3.9 to 6 in forest soils. Water depth is increased. The water table rises, which may improve growing conditions for pastures, crops and wetland vegetation.

The beaver has been successfully restored to many sites throughout mainland Europe (about 100 during the 20th century at the last count), so that there is now much practical experience for us to draw on. Moreover, the EU's so-called 'Species and Habitats Directive' calls upon member states to consider the feasibility of reintroducing extinct indigenous mammals such as wolves, bears and beavers. With this in mind in the 1990s Scottish Natural Heritage (SNH) began the process of investigating whether the beaver could return to Scotland, following the World Conservation Union's (IUCN) Reintroduction Guidelines.

Although the IUCN guidelines have evolved into a complex document, their main points are as follows:
1. It must be established that the species was once indigenous to the country or region from fossil, specimen and historical records.
2. The reasons for extinction must be known and must no longer occur in the area to which animals are to be returned.
3. The most closely related living population should be used for the reintroduction, but removal of individuals from this population must not be damaging to its long-term survival. Reintroduction must also not harm populations of other native species.
4. Sufficient suitable habitat must exist or be recreated for a sustainable population to develop.
5. Potential areas of conflict with local people must be considered and plans must be implemented to ensure that they do not suffer.
6. Support from local people for the reintroduction is necessary by creating awareness and educating people as to the effects any re-introduction will have on them.

In the case of Scotland we know already that fossils and historical records show that beavers thrived there from soon after the end of the last Ice Age until less than 500 years ago (see p.108). We also know that extinction was most probably as a result of hunting for fur, meat and/or castoreum rather than habitat loss, except perhaps locally. However, that still left many unanswered questions. Therefore SNH called upon a wide range of research expertise to find out these vitally important answers.

Taxonomic problems

As we have seen there are several morphologically distinct populations of beaver in Europe today. Which one should be used for reintroduction? With John Lynch from Arizona State University I decided to compare the skulls of Britain's extinct beavers with those of Europe's extant populations; the most similar in size and shape of skull would probably be the best one for reintroduction as it would suggest a close genetic and evolutionary relationship. I began to measure hundreds of beaver skulls from museums collections in Britain, Germany and the Swedish University

of Agricultural Sciences in Sweden. Also colleagues in other museums, including Sylke Frahnert from Germany and Géraldine Veron and Jean-Louis Senotier from France very kindly sent me measurements from skulls they had measured. After 10,000 measurements from more than 300 skulls, both ancient and modern, John Lynch began a complex multivariate statistical analysis of the data. We found that modern French, German and Scandinavian beavers had skulls that were distinctly different. When we compared the average size and shape of mandibles from extinct English beavers with these modern ones, we found that they were very similar to Scandinavian beavers; the single Scottish jaw bone was also very similar. A similar result was seen for the skull too, except that rather anomalously the three Scottish specimens were either more like French or German beaver skulls. This kind of result often happens where sample sizes are low and individuals may not resemble the former population. However, overall we could state categorically that on skull morphology Britain's former beavers most resembled those living today in Scandinavia and therefore Scandinavian beavers should be used for any reintroduction to Scotland. This seemed to make sense to us, because in terms of climate and habitat, there are many similarities between Scotland and Scandinavia so that reintroduced beavers would be pre-adapted to life here.

Hydrology

Beavers are keystone species that affect not only the riparian vegetation through feeding, but also the flow of water through river systems. Unfortunately there has been little research specifically into the effects of beavers on the hydrology of water courses, and most of this research was applied to the North American species. Dr Angela Gurnell of the University of Birmingham reviewed the effect that dam building has on hydrology and attempted to predict/model the likely consequences of reintroducing beavers to three sites in Scotland. Her very detailed study concluded that beavers would be likely to have little impact on the hydrology of rivers and streams in Scotland.

Of the three sites that she examined, only the River Dee supported sufficient deciduous woodland for beavers, although some small streams were noted with appropriate tree cover in sheltered, lower gradient sites along the bottoms of valleys. Also the three sites could support burrow construction (rather than just lodges), although the conditions were not ideal for these, except again possibly on the River Dee floodplain, which had finer sediments in side channels. The potential sites also had fast-flowing rivers which would be unlikely to support beavers, except on side channels where the water flow is gentler or still and the sediment finer, and where dams could easily be constructed to produce small beaver ponds. Even here the rate of sediment deposition would probably fill these ponds quickly, if the dams were not destroyed by rocks and other debris being carried downstream during the spate. The prediction that beavers would select minor tributaries or floodplains (as they do in many parts of their existing range) suggests that beavers would have minimal hydrological, fluvial and geomorphological impacts on the main river channels. The most significant impact would be an increase in areas of open water and wetland on floodplains, and a change in the species composition and tree cover of deciduous trees as a result of tree felling and waterlogging of soil by rising water levels.

Woodlands

One concern in a country that has amongst the lowest woodland cover in Europe, is that beavers would clear cut large areas of riparian woodland. Dr Peter Reynolds investigated this aspect of potential beaver impact. Much commercial forestry in Scotland comprises conifers and the good news is that beavers rarely fell, eat or debark conifers, much less settle in areas bounded by coniferous woodland. Even where flooding caused by dams might cause loss of conifers indirectly these can easily be overcome by local drainage schemes or removal of problem beavers. However, it should be borne in mind that between 1988 and 1993 the Swiss government only paid out the equivalent of £3,623 of compensation (about 30-50% of the actual costs) for all damage caused by its 350 beavers, of which forestry constituted only 10% of this amount. This compares with more than half a million pounds paid out for damage caused by wild pigs (*Sus scrofa*). So we can be pretty confident that beavers should not affect commercial forestry significantly.

It was much less clear what the effect of beavers would be on native or semi-natural broad-leaved woodland. In Scandinavia, over browsing by moose and beavers may prevent regeneration of native woodland, but this does not occur in all areas and often beavers produce suitable alternative food sources for deer. It cannot be predicted what, if any, combined browsing of red and roe deer with beavers would have on Scottish woodlands. However, it is essential that this is monitored and that management plans are in place to control deer and beaver numbers where necessary. Peter Reynolds concluded that on balance the beavers are of significant benefit, because of their role in the management and creation of wet woodland ecosystems in Scotland; this should assist the Forestry Commission in its attempt to implement the Woodland Habitat Action Plans arising from Biodiversity Action Plans to promote semi-natural woodland and also the riparian zone policy of the Forestry Commission's Forest and Water Guidelines. And all with no human effort! What could be better?

Problems with fish

Anglers may be very hostile to the return of the beaver, because of a common belief that the activities of beavers will in some way affect fish numbers. The Atlantic salmon (*Salmo salar*) has been declining in numbers for many years and the causes of this are various and hotly disputed. Trout (*Salmo trutta*) numbers have also declined due to various causes including acidification of streams. Many anglers believe that the beaver may just push the salmon population over the edge, despite the fact that salmon and beavers have co-existed for many thousands of years.

Salmon and trout fishing are important leisure industries in Scotland and it is vital that beavers do not affect these adversely. Peter Collen of the Freshwater Fisheries Laboratory in Pitlochry reviewed the evidence for SNH for any impact that beavers have on fish. However, much of the research that has been carried out concerns North American beavers and may not be directly relevant to a European situation.

Peter Collen concluded that it was difficult to come to any firm conclusions on the impact of beavers on the ecology and movements of native fish. The available evidence suggested that beavers could be beneficial, by improving water quality through dams, increasing the abundance and diversity of freshwater invertebrates on which fish feed, and reducing the effect of hydrological extremes through dams regulating water flow. However, beavers may also be harmful because very large dams might prevent fish migrations (although Eurasian beavers tend to build only small dams), the beaver ponds may cause silting up of good spawning sites and better habitat for fish-eating animals such as pike, otters and mergansers (*Mergus* spp.) could result in loss of juvenile fish in particular.

Finally, he suggested that the level of beaver impact may depend on the size of the water course in question. In treeless areas, beavers would be expected to have little impact, because beaver population densities would be very low. In areas with riparian woodland, but where the streams are currently too small for angling, beavers may create useful pond habitats, which could be used for angling. Where beavers may dam streams, it is possible that the dams could prevent fish migration (at certain times of year at least) and anglers might complain about getting their

Managing Ham Fen Reserve in Kent

The beaver probably became extinct in Kent more than 1,000 years ago, but in late 2001 two Norwegian beaver families were released into the Kent Wildlife Trust's Ham Fen Reserve. Although the beavers are being left to their own devices, this was not a reintroduction as the reserve has been fenced to keep the beavers in.

Ham Fen Reserve is almost 4 hectares in area and lies between Sandwich and Deal in the parish of Worth in Kent. It is an old fen with a deep peat layer, which is being invaded by birch and alder trees, but it also supports interesting vegetation such as the marsh fern (Thelypteris thelypteroides) *and the saw sedge* (Cladium mariscus), *which have restricted distributions.*

One way of preventing Ham Fen from becoming totally overgrown by woodland vegetation would be to use volunteers to remove the trees

and scrub. However, Kent Wildlife Trust is aiming to use the concept of Near Natural Areas (NNAs) to manage its and neighbouring land. NNAs were first developed in the Netherlands and use large grazing and browsing mammals such as cattle and horses to manage sustainably areas of natural vegetation. The Kent Wildlife Trust and the Wildwood Centre are extending this idea to aquatic ecosystems by using beavers to try to manage sustainably the vegetation and increase the biodiversity of Ham Fen Reserve. The current trial is to run for five years and will monitor the beavers and their effects on the fen.

Hopefully, if this experiment is successful, others will take the opportunity to use beavers in a similar way leading ultimately to the reintroduction of the beaver in England.

tackle snagged on cut wood etc. in the streams, but again the creation of large beaver ponds might benefit anglers by providing areas suitable for migrating salmon and resident trout. On rivers that are too wide for damming, beavers would again be expected to have little impact on angling, except perhaps by causing a snagging hazard. So, overall beavers are likely to be beneficial to fish populations, but some problems may arise, which will have to be dealt with appropriately.

What do the public think?

An important component of any reintroduction is to consult the public on their views. Without public, especially local, support, reintroductions are very likely to fail. In 1997 SNH contracted Scott Porter Research and Marketing to survey public opinion on the beaver's potential return to Scotland. The survey consulted three main groups:

1. Consultees from interested organisations who would be expected to support or not the reintroduction.
2. Pro-active public who wanted to voice their opinions on the matter and were provided with a means to do so.
3. Passive public who were asked their opinion, but would not otherwise have responded.
   Two questions were asked:

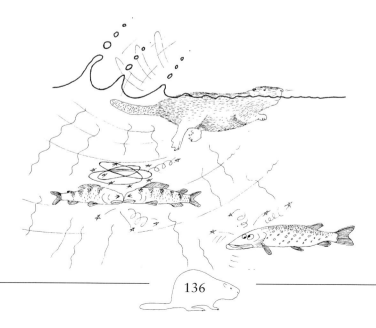

1. Do you support a proposal to restore the European beaver to the wild in Scotland?
2. If so, do you support such a reintroduction beginning during the next three years.

All three groups supported the reintroduction of the beaver, but the level of support in each group depended on their interests. The consultees with an academic or conservation background tended to strongly support beaver reintroduction because it provided an opportunity to increase biodiversity, eco-tourism and our moral obligation to restore a native species. Those against a reintroduction were worried about managing beavers afterwards and anglers/fishermen were particularly strongly against. Of the pro-active public more than 86% supported the return of the beaver, but again, many of these people had a conservation interest. Support was positive overall, but much less strong in those who have an interest in forestry, water and riparian habitats, and land management. Farmers, anglers and others with fishing interests were strongly against the proposal.

Of the passive public more than four times as many people supported reintroduction as were against, but a quarter of people did not express a view either way. The reasons for and against reintroduction were similar to those for the consultees and pro-active public.

Overall, therefore, the Scottish public is strongly for a reintroduction of the beaver in Scotland in the next three years. However, some groups, notably anglers, were very much against it, and clearly more research and education is required to overcome these points of view. However, this should not stop an attempt to reintroduce beavers, because we are only going to find out the pros and cons from our actual experiences. Experiences elsewhere in Europe suggest that problems are likely to be small and benefits great. Moreover, our European colleagues have already come up with a wide variety of solutions to beaver problems. So full steam ahead!

Finding a site

Scotland may not be a very big country, but finding suitable habitat for beavers could take a very long time. SNH asked the Institute of Terrestrial Ecology at Banchory to investigate new methods for finding good beaver habitat in Scotland. Instead of tramping around the countryside, the ITE team used Geographical Information System (GIS) data to analyse those areas that seem to have the best environmental factors for beavers. GIS databases contain information about anything, but stored spatially (e.g. regionally, nationally or globally). This could include habitat types, road systems, rainfall, topography, etc. By combining data from different datasets and knowledge of how the beaver's presence is affected by these environmental factors, it is possible to look at the correlation between them to come up with the best sites available. In this case, ITE combined data on terrestrial habitats, water and wetlands, and topography (height above sea-level) to come up with 770 km² of riparian broadleaf woodland (excluding the urbanised central belt of Scotland), which might provide potential beaver habitat. Most of this suitable habitat was centred on the Ness, Spey, Tay, Dee/Don and Lomond river systems, which suggested that these areas could support a recolonising beaver population without the need to artificially move animals around or create habitat corridors. It was estimated that these areas could support up to 1,000 beavers.

Now that the field had been narrowed down and specific areas had been identified, it was necessary to explore the scene on the ground to see if these areas were actually as good as suggested by the GIS study. David Macdonald and his colleagues at Oxford University were asked by SNH to come up with a protocol for identifying good beaver release sites. They used a simple scoring system for recording whether a particular site had all the essential physical and environmental elements that we know beavers like elsewhere in Europe. This included various hydrological factors, vegetation needs, human effects and the potential for the beavers to disperse elsewhere. The scoring system was then applied to nine sites selected by SNH as possibly being suitable for beavers. Of these only three sites scored highly enough to be regarded as really good beaver habitats and two of these were surveyed in detail on the ground. It was estimated that those two sites combined could support an estimated beaver population of 10 to 30 beaver families, but these small populations would not be self-sustaining in the long-term.

'Why don't they use canals like we do?'

Finally, the key environmental and physical factors were used to develop a GIS model to predict where beavers might spread in Scotland and how well populations might develop and survive over time. The model predicted that population growth and spread from the two potential release sites would be slow, owing to a lack of suitable adjacent habitat, so that even 50 years after reintroduction population densities of beavers might be very low. This would make the reintroduced beaver population very susceptible to catastrophes such as disease or even road traffic accidents, which could severely limit population expansion and may even result in extinction.

Knapdale, a trial reintroduction

In late 2001 Scottish Natural Heritage applied for a licence from the Scottish Executive for the trial reintroduction of Eurasian beavers to Knapdale Forest in Argyll. If all goes well, the beavers will be imported from Scandinavia in the autumn of 2002, when they will be quarantined before final release in the spring of 2003.

In 2000 SNH decided to work with the Forestry Commission to try and identify a suitable trial site for reintroducing beavers. There is a clear logistical advantage for SNH, because only one land owner is involved, who is supportive of the reintroduction. Using a refined version of ITE's GIS analysis, several sites owned by the Forestry Commission were identified for follow-up field

work. After all this careful analysis, Knapdale Forest was finally chosen as the best site. Local consultation followed in order to create awareness of the beaver reintroduction and to get that very vital local support.

Knapdale Forest near Lochgoilhead in Argyll is within a National Scenic Area. It is bounded by water on two sides, the Crinan Canal in the north and the Sound of Jura and Loch Sween in the west. Although the forest covers about 50 km² much of this is dominated by conifers and is therefore unsuitable for beavers. However there is a core area of 15-20 km², which is made up of low hills and valleys interspersed with small to medium-sized lochs interconnected by burns. The riparian woodland is dominated by broadleaves, includ-

ing birch, willow and oak, with also some alder, rowan and hazel, and there is a well-developed ground vegetation. All in all this makes ideal beaver habitat, but surrounded by conifers and isolated from other beaver habitat, it is hoped that the beavers will remain local during the trial rather than dispersing over a wide area. Time will tell, but we should never underestimate them.

SNH intends to release up to three beaver families giving a total of up to 18 individuals into Knapdale. Again, by releasing in well-established social groups, the aim is to avoid unnecessary dispersal. Release sites have been selected 0.8 to 2.5 km apart to take into account how much riparian woodland a beaver group needs and allow some space for dispersal within the forest. However, how SNH uses artificial lodges or other methods to try and prevent groups splitting up and dispersing has not yet been decided, although there is much we can learn from reintroductions in Europe. If any beavers do wander further afield, they will be captured and brought back to Knapdale. In all Knapdale has been estimated to be able to support a beaver population varying from 15 to 60, with an average of about 25-30. However, habitat manage-ment is already being imple-mented to increase the area of suitable habitat available for beavers so that during the course of the trial, the carrying capacity of Knapdale will hopefully increase as the population of beavers increases.

As Knapdale is a trial reintro-duction, SNH have decided on three ways in which to decide whether it has been a success. Firstly, the population will be closely monitored to see if similar survival occurs as in successful reintroductions elsewhere in Europe. Secondly, an assessment will be made as to whether damage to the ecosys-tem caused by beaver activities has been significant and unsus-tainable. Finally, there will be an assessment as to whether there has been a significant impact on local land use by people and whether the cost of any damage exceeds expectations signifi-cantly.

Let us all hope that the Knapdale trial is so successful that before it concludes, SNH will recommend the release of more beavers at other sites in Scotland.

I am looking forward to the day, when we can say to Scot-land's first reintroduced beavers 'Welcome back, it has been too long since we last saw you here.'

Bibliography

Collen, P. (1997). Review of the potential impacts of re-introducing Eurasian beaver *Castor fiber* L. on the ecology and movement of native fishes, and the likely implications for current angling practices in Scotland. *Scottish Natural Heritage Research, Survey and Monitoring Report* No. 86.

Gurnell, A.M. (1997). Analysis of the effects of beaver dam-building activities on local hydrology. *Scottish Natural Heritage Research, Survey and Monitoring Report* No. 85.

Hammerson, G.A. (1994). Beaver (*Castor canadensis*): Ecosystem alterations, management and monitoring. *Natural Areas Journal* **14(1)**: 44-57.

Hartman, G. (1992). Age determination of live beaver by dental x-ray. *Wildlife Society Bulletin* **20**: 216-220.

Hartman, G. (1995). Patterns of spread of a reintroduced beaver *Castor fiber* population in Sweden. *Wildlife Biology* **1**: 97-103.

Hartman, G. (1996). Habitat selection by European beaver (*Castor fiber*) colonizing a boreal landscape. *Journal of Zoology London* **240**: 317-325.

Jakobsson, K. (1981). Impact of beaver (*Castor fiber* L.) on riverside vegetation at Pälböleån, N. Sweden. *Wahlenbergia* **7**: 89-98.

Jenkins, S.H. & Busher, P.E. (1979). *Castor canadensis. Mammalian Species* **120**: 1-8.

Kitchener, A.C. & Conroy, J.W.H. (1997). The history of the Eurasian beaver *Castor fiber* in Scotland. *Mammal Review* **27**: 95-108.

Kitchener, A.C. & Lynch, J.M. (2000). A morphometric comparison of the skulls of fossil British and extant European beavers, *Castor fiber. Scottish Natural Heritage Research, Survey and Monitoring Report* No. 127.

Macdonald, D.W., Tattersall, F.H., Brown, E.D. & Balharry, D. (1995). Reintroducing the European beaver to Britain: Nostalgic meddling or restoring biodiversity. *Mammal Review* **25(4)**: 161-201.

Marcuzzi, G. (1986). Man-beaver relations. *Investigations on beavers* **5**: 16-72.

Novak, M., Baker, J.A., Obbard, M.E. & Malloch, B. (1987). *Wild furbearer management and conservation in North America.* Ontario: Ministry of Natural Resources.

Ognev, S.I. (1963). *Mammals of the USSR and adjacent countries. Vol. V.* pp. 286-371. Jerusalem: Israel Program for Scientific Translations.

Reynolds, P. (2000). European beaver and woodland habitats: a review. *Scottish Natural Heritage Research, Survey and Monitoring Report* No. 126.

Rosell, F. & Pedersen, K.V. (1999). *Bever.* Landbrukforlaget.

Rosell, F. & Sun, L. (1999). Use of anal gland secretion to distinguish the two beaver species *Castor canadensis* and *C, fiber. Wildlife Biology* 5:119-123.

Savage, R.J.G. & Long, M.L. (1987). *The evolution of mammals.* London: British Museum (Natural History).

Scott Porter Research & Marketing Ltd. (1998). Re-introduction of the European beaver to Scotland: Results of a public consultation. *Scottish Natural Heritage Research, Survey and Monitoring Report* No. 121.

Wilsson, L. (1971). Observations and experiments on the ethology of the European beaver (*Castor fiber* L.). *Viltrevy* 8: 113-266.

Yalden, D. (1999). *The history of British mammals.* London: Poyser.

Index

Activity 71
Ageing, methods 105-106
Agnotocastor 15
Anal glands 75-6, 89
Anal gland secretion 21, 77
Annual movements 71
Aquatic adaptations 18-21

Baculum 87,89
Beaver beetle 17, 103
Beaver hats 115-118
Beaver-rat 12-13
Bibliography 141-2
Bipedal walking 27, 46, 94
Birth weights 91
Body weights 14
Building behaviours 41, 47-8
Building materials 40
  transport of 40, 46
Burrows 32, 81

Caches 68-9, 85
Canals 33-4, 81
Castoreum 25, 75-7
  components 76
  deposition of 77
  medicinal properties 114

Castoroides 15-16
Castor sacs 25, 75-6, 89
Chambers
  feeding 32, 37
  sleeping 32
Cloaca 24, 25, 75, 89
Coecotrophy 24, 66-7
Collecting food 59-60
Coprophagy 24

Daimonelix 15
Dams 30, 43, 85-6
  acoustic stimuli 46
  building of 44-5
  dimensions 44-5
Dancing 99, 100
Development of kits 91, 93
  behaviours 95
  building 41, 48
  digging 31
  feeding 70
  food selection 70
  galloping 27
  grooming 74
  predator avoidance 83
  scent marking 79
  tail slapping 28

walking 27
Diet 54
  anti-herbivory compounds 57-59
  geographical variation in 57
  nutrients 58
  summer 55
  winter 56
Differences between species 8
Digestive efficiency 24
Digging 30
Dispersal 71, 85-6, 102
Diving 27, 28, 29
Diving physiology 21
Drinking 66

Effects on landscapes 49-53
Evolution 15-17
Exploitation in North America 119-122
Exploratory behaviour 96

Fighting 96-7, 99
Foraging distances 52
Fossil beavers 15-17, 108-109

Galloping 27
Geographical distribution 8, 10-11
Gestation periods 90
Giant beavers 15-17
Gnawing 66
Grooming 72-73
  mutual 95, 97, 99, 100, 101
Grooming claw 20-21, 73

Ham Fen Reserve 135
Handling food 64-5
Herbivorous adaptations 22-4
History in Britain 108-111
History in Europe 107
Hybridisation 8

Keystone species 49
Kits, transport of 94
Knapdale 139-140

Litter sizes 90-91
  effect of habitats 91
Lodges 30, 45, 81, 85-6
  bank 31, 35-6
  brook 35-7
  building 34, 38-40
  dimensions 38
  internal temperatures 34
  occupation 34
Longevity 105

Management 123-4
Maternal care 93
Mating
  behaviour 90
  seasonality 88
Milk composition 93
Mites 103,104
Moulting fur 21
Mountain beaver 12-13
Mortality 105

Near Natural Areas 135
Nematodes 17, 104
North American beavers
  introductions to Britain 112-113

Oestrous cycles 90
Oestrus 90

Pair formation 102
Palaeocastor 15
Parasites 103-104
Ponds, duration of 53
Predators 81-82
  escape from 81

Rearing kits 85
Recipe 129
Reintroductions 123
  angling, impacts on 134-5
  Britain 130
  ecological benefits 130-131
  economic impacts 123
  effects on hydrology 132-3

finding a site 137-8
genetic variability 127-8
habitat needs 127, 137-8
IUCN guidelines 131
population increases 127
public consultation 136-9
recolonisation 124-7
taxonomy 131-2
woodlands, impacts on 133-4
Reproduction 88-90

Scent glands 75-6
Scent marking 75, 77-8
Scent matching 80
Scent mounds 78-79, 96
Sewellel see Mountain beaver
Sexing beavers 87-89
Sexual maturity 88
Species of beaver 8
Social behaviours 97
Social groups 85
Subspecies of beaver 10-11
Suckling 92
Swimming 27, 29
Swimming speed 29

Temporary nests 34
Tail, fat storage 20, 69

Tail slapping 28, 83-4
Tail, swimming and diving 28
Tail, thermoregulation 20
Territorial defence 75, 78
Territories, establishment of 86
Threat behaviours 96
Tooth sharpening 23, 61, 63, 66
Tooth wear 23
Teeth 22-3
  milk 91
Ticks 21, 104
Trails 59-60
Tree felling 52, 54, 60-62
Tree sampling 57
Trees, maximum diameter felled 60-61
Trematodes 104
Trogontherium 17, 108
Tularaemia 104
Tunnels 32

Uterus masculinus 87-8

Vocalisations 98-9

Walking 27
Whiskers 23
Wrestling 100,101